THE MAN-WOMAN GAME

Man-Woman Symbol
(A fusion of ♀ and ♂)

THE MAN-WOMAN GAME

The fulfillment of woman.
The triumph of man.

Leo Gorelkin, M.D.
with Paula Gorelkin

PRINCIPIO PRESS
Atlanta, 1990

Published by:

Principio Press
P.O. Box 95-764
Atlanta, GA 30347

Library of Congress Catalog Number 90-61721

ISBN 0-9626938-4-7

Printed in the United States of America

DEDICATION

To Paula—
Without whom this book would not have been written or even contemplated; and whose love and inspiration are a perpetual beacon, shining through the confusion and unhappiness of life, leading to its greater pleasures and joys,

and

To men and women everywhere.

ACKNOWLEDGEMENT

Our thanks to Dr. Victor Baranco, More University, and its teachers, whose enlightened principles are the foundation of this book.

Our thanks to our editor, Eve F. Shulmister, whose professionalism, suggestions and support are greatly appreciated.

Thanks also to Peggy Lamberson and David Marcus for their helpful review of the manuscript.

The puzzle to the path of
happiness has two equal, perfectly
fitting, but very different parts:
man and woman.

Put them together
and the mystery disappears.

L.G.

TABLE OF CONTENTS

INTRODUCTION

This is not just another "HOW TO" or "FIX IT" book. It's a book that simply explains what is. Understanding and accepting what is clears the path to happiness.

We live in a society riddled with much unhappiness. The latest statistic on divorce, the latest picture of the singles' scene, the deluge of articles, books, T.V. programs on "How To:" lose weight, exercise, get a man, keep a man, make love, fall in love, and stay in love all point to one thing, a voracious need for answers. What a hunger!

Let's look at life as a field on which various games are played. The most critical and universal game of life is the man-woman game. It goes on all the time, starting from earliest childhood, at work or at play, whether we want it, are aware of it, or not.

Of course one needn't play if one chooses to be a hermit. But for the rest of us, we're in it. Best play to win. Mind you, when we say to win we're not talking about bettering or beating someone, since the man-woman game is won by the union of the players, not the dominance of one over the other.

Once we're in this game, two factors become critical: 1) that we have the desire and intention to win and, 2) that we know the rules of the game. The difficulty here is that most of us actively play by a set of learned, deeply ingrained rules and with views of relating that insure our loss. Remember all that hunger?

For example, if you were playing football, wanted to win, and knew the rules of the game, you wouldn't opt to punt on the first down. Not a winning strategy.

This book not only proposes to tell you what is *really* happening on the playing field, but also alerts you to the real rules of the game.

Some people may either not want to play or not want to win. This book is not for them. If you choose to play and win, it won't always be easy to *see the light*. Yet when you do, it will be blinding in its truth, empowering you to form lasting relationships with deepening love and understanding.

This book does not address mental illness. It is not intended to be psychotherapeutic or analytic. However, we *do* intend to impart certain principles of reality, as we see it, to couples and individuals who want to enrich their lives and enhance their relationships.

As a means of illustration, this book is also peppered with the personal anecdotes of a couple who embraced these principles, the discovery and acceptance for which they are eternally grateful.

PROLOGUE

First Impressions—His

Something had obviously happened. Two of our close friends were quite suddenly exhibiting heightened pleasure in each other and an enjoyment of life that was irresistibly appealing, especially to Paula. Dorothy appeared more beautiful and attractive than ever, with a glow about her, while Cary exuded an air of calm self-assurance as he doted over her. They were like two newlyweds, kids, excited and bubbling over with joy in each other. The air was electric, the aura compelling. They had taken a couple of courses by teachers from a place called More University, in California. These courses, they told us, had drastically and most happily changed their lives.

Who were these people from California and what where these courses? It was something I certainly couldn't ignore with impunity. Nor did I want to, so taken was I too, with the charm and aura of this change. Furthermore, Paula had given me strong signals that she really wanted some of this *stuff*.

Here, too, is an important example of how the man/woman game really works. The woman in my life wanted something very much; thus, for both our sakes it was wise, indeed, for me to sit up and take notice. So what about these classes? Oh, teachers would be coming into Atlanta to conduct them in the near future.

Mind you, our friends were happily married before being exposed to all this "good stuff"—a straight pair of folks, punctilious, very successful and respected classical musicians. So they apparently weren't going off the deep end, but really seemed to be getting so much more out of their lives.

Okay, let's see, two courses were to be taught. First, *Basic Sensuality*, then *Man-Woman* would be offered in the future sometime. There was a short blurb on these. *Basic Sensuality* read, "a two-day course on the application of the principles of the More philosophy as it pertains to sensuality . . . provides information and methods for enhancing and expanding the extent and intensity of sensual ecstasy. . ."

Did you see that? "Sensual ecstasy"? What a scary idea: visions of Sodom & Gomorrah; my wife, an insatiable sexual creature, the stuff nightmares are made of. Most threatening was the idea that all this would open a Pandora's box of sexual appetites in my wife which I couldn't satisfy or control. Who were they to imply that my very close, caring, loving and happy marriage of 22 years wasn't up to snuff? If it ain't broke, why fix it? Thanks a lot, guys!

My initial warm and curious interest quickly turned to fear and hostility. Who needs this? Need it or not, the die was cast. Paula remained quite interested. The situation wouldn't go away and couldn't be ignored. I felt that I had been thrust into a battle to preserve my marriage, to defend my manhood, and you could be sure I would fight.

I tried to play it cool and feel my way along. Eventually the teachers came into town to teach *Basic Sensuality*. Luckily, the weekend of the course was one in which we couldn't attend, as Paula was giving a concert Saturday evening—a reprieve. There was, however, a Friday evening question and answer introduction to the course.

Safe enough. Although I was somewhat apprehensive, I was still a bit curious, and with my typical hubris, was going to take these guys down a few notches. If I could only discredit these teachers in some way, these courses wouldn't seem so important.

To my dismay, this didn't happen. There were three of them: two women and a man—slick, attractive, and articulate. I could neither rattle them nor embarrass them.

Paula seemed quite taken by it all; so much so that she toyed with the idea of totally breaking with tradition and taking the course that same weekend, in spite of her upcoming concert. I talked her out of it—a truce and just a delay, not the best nor the worst of outcomes.

Our weekend for *Basic Sensuality* finally did come. We attended the Friday night introduction again. This time Paula and I sat apart. I still felt threatened and was hostile. I blamed Paula for putting us there and think I might have been angry with her; hard now to remember exactly.

That was about two years ago. Our marriage has not only survived this, but has blossomed in ways we never conceived of. How and why, I truly hope will become clear in the following pages.

First Impressions—Hers

"Now, remember honey, we're not going to the course, this weekend. We're just going for the introductory session, this time, to see if it's something to do in the future." Those were Leo's words, as he hoped to secure my ready compliance, even before we had arrived at the session.

As the evening progressed, I felt more and more in the presence of Truth with a capital T; the other side of a new world already partially revealed to me through meditation. Desire for this information so welled up in me that even though there was a concert to perform the next night, I actually considered spending "concert day" totally out of routine. That meant neither going near a piano, nor spending time mentally immersed in preparations for the concert.

But Leo remained steadfast and I was grateful. After all, I did want the concert to go well. And that goal did require going through my usual preparations.

Leo was a good producer in my life! I had spotted him almost immediately as a *life saver*—a guy who had it all together and had the wherewithal to make me happy for a long time to come. He was always there for the important things—delivering right on schedule. Marriage, even though he was full of trepidation; a child; a Master's degree in Music, when we had no money to pay for it. The list is a long one and included lots of affection and a healthy satisfying sex life.

So what was I seeking? Two of our close friends had exhibited greater intimacy after taking some More courses. Cary seemed to respond to Dorothy's most casual whims, like a sergeant-at-arms. Very appealing. And I wanted some.

The next occasion Leo and I had to attend *Basic Sensuality* was that winter, about 4 months after our first session. We enrolled in the course, and wanting to hear every word, we attended the introduction, as well. We sat on opposite sides of the room—unusual for us. There were four teachers—2 couples: two major teachers and their assistants.

One thing stands out very clearly in memory. The male teacher, handsome, intelligent and articulate, asked us to say our names and what had brought us there. When it was Leo's turn, he gesticulated broadly towards me across the room, saying that he wasn't there under his own volition but was there because of me. "Very wise of you", the teacher responded. "Odd," I thought, feeling a tiny bit guilty for having dragged Leo there and somewhat surprised at his hostile tone of voice.

We were both somewhat skeptical about what we could possibly learn of real value after 22 years of happy married life. Yet we had agreed that we had nothing to lose. I had little idea of how threatened Leo felt at that time, and in fact was hoping to find ways to give him more sexual pleasure. I was also hoping we would come across some information that would allow me to feel less guilty about mine. I figured if these were the only goals accomplished during the weekend, it would be worth the time and expense.

In fact, much more was about to occur. Our life together would be forever changed and for the better.

A UNION OF ALIENS

1

A woman's happiness is directly proportional to her getting what she wants.
A man's happiness is directly proportional to his winning—which is determined by his woman's happiness.

L.G.

This is what the goal of the man-woman game is all about: the pleasurable union—both emotional and physical—of two equal but very different beings. The origin of these differences is not just biological, but also cultural and historical. The biological differences are wondrous, and the potential source of great pleasures. Yet the gender differences enforced by our culture can create obstacles to the goal of a lasting and fulfilling union.

For centuries we have perpetuated and accentuated a host of cultural myths and paradigms as beacons of these gender differences. At the same time, we complain about their existence. Both man and woman, in some ways, want the other to be more like themselves and go about punishing the other for a lack of compliance.

"Why can't a woman be more like a man?" sings Henry Higgins in the musical *My Fair Lady*. While this sentiment may be cute, it is also tragic in its support of the myth of male superiority. Women have been second class citizens for centuries and we have all been paying the price for this folly in ways both overt and perniciously subtle.

Perhaps at no other period in modern times have such attitudes been more insidiously developed and supported than during the scientific and industrial revolutions of the eighteenth and nineteenth centuries. For here, the notion of male superiority went beyond the obvious matter of brute strength. Disguised by the cloak of scientific respectability, the myth of male superiority entered the more subtle and sophisticated realm of the intellect. For example, it was considered that the larger male skull, encasing a larger brain, was obviously the basis of male superior intelligence. Thus, even though girls seem to learn to read faster than boys, their grasp and retention was supposedly fleeting. That of the boys however, would be profound and lasting.

Observing the countless numbers of vigorous and highly motile male sperm as sharply contrasted with the seemingly inferior, single and sluggish female egg, men busily set about developing pseudo-scientific, self-serving theories.

To be sure, we have begun to clear the weeds from the culture garden of these gender based paradigms, as women approach equal treatment by society. But deeply rooted ideas die hard. We start to see why the man-woman game is such a tough one to play and win. And win/win is the only fulfilling outcome.

Although differences do exist, this is not a competition. If one partner loses, then both ultimately lose.

Once recognized and appreciated, such gender differences can be played with and used as tools for success. Notwithstanding all the books and advice about the way a man and woman should relate, men and women are not allies, but aliens. That is why the 50-50 "I get mine—you get yours" formula works only for some and fails for many.

Even for couples who master such formats of compromise in relating to each other, there really is much more to be had. In the truly meaningful man-woman relationship, gratification is its own reward. Once achieved, the goal has been reached! What we actually mean by this will become clear as we explore the wonderful and challenging differences between us.

For example, while we perceive ourselves to be

communicating well, men and women often speak different languages and have different thoughts. These differences may create confusion between us, and are the source of much frustration and discord.

At times the product of such differences is blatantly obvious:

It was during a recent trip to New York that, as was our wont, we were wending our way up Madison Avenue, wandering in and out of art galleries. We enjoyed our browsing and sometimes even toyed with the idea of buying a work of art. The fantasy of ownership was exciting. At times we found ourselves engaged in interesting and cordial conversations with some of the gallery owners.

This particular gallery was strong in realist European paintings. One of the owners, an attractive young woman, was on hand (her partner and husband being off on business) and offered to explain the backgrounds of the paintings currently on view. The canvas directly in front of us was beautifully executed. It showed the edge of a bed post. There was a chair, upon which lay a plumed gentlemen's hat of eighteenth century vintage. There was also a young woman, looking back into the room over her shoulder, coquettishly. She was in the act of locking the door to the room.

The owner explained that she and her husband often played with naming such paintings. In this instance, her husband's title was "No Escape". Her title was "Romantic Tryst".

We were quite amused by this—such a striking example of how men and women, even when given the same object, often perceive and interpret it so differently. Think of how wildly things can go astray from *different* starting places!

For certain we know there are gender based differences between men and women. Yet as such, they do not indicate the superiority of one sex over the other. Instead these differences are complementary, and when properly fused they result in harmony. Therefore it becomes important to recognize what the differences are, and how they work. Then they may become a source of energy for deeper, happier relationships, rather than a source of disruption.

Let's look more specifically at what some of these differences in language and thought are.

Different Languages, Different Thoughts

The qualities we attribute to men and women here are not mutually exclusive. That is, both sexes can cross over in their modes of thinking and often do. So these concepts are generalities, patterns within the context of how a man and woman usually relate to one another.

A man's thinking in this context tends to be rational, organized and end point oriented—often restricted to the job at hand. Beautifully designed to get the job done. Guys are success junkies and very much need to be winners.

It begins well before that adolescent fantasy of scoring the winning touchdown in a big game, and being the hero, adored and desired by the girl of his dreams. Getting the job done in the fastest, most efficient way is a sure path to success. The concern is how and why things work the way they do.

This straight line thinking isn't all that much fun in itself. The excitement lies in attaining the goal, the end point, i.e. it is very production oriented.

Remember, we do not exclude women from among those who are capable of rational thought, or those having the ability to get a job done, etc. Our point is just that *within the context of the man-woman game* things work best when the guy is allowed to do what he does best—production.

Now, viewed within the same context, a woman's thought process tends to appear more circuitous (a man's view), panoramic, more encompassing, and less linear, with more levels and meanings at once. Have you ever noticed how often men seem not to really understand what a woman means when she says something (especially when she's communicating with other women)? It's almost as if women have a language of their own which men often cannot follow.

Women are not often concerned with how things work. Their major interest is that it does work; with using it, not fixing it! She's more a consumer than a producer. Here we've touched on gender roles and dynamics—an important topic for further discussion (Chapter 3: *ROLES AND DYNAMICS IN THE MAN-WOMAN GAME*).

How often have you noticed that when a woman asks a man for one thing, she often gets something else? Proper connections, shared perceptions and understanding between the sexes are clearly often not achieved. Men too often seem not to get the message. This is not always from lack of trying. Men really want to win with their women, though at times it may appear to be otherwise!

A woman's language often makes use of a code. It's really tough for a logically oriented guy (especially when he's not in the know) to understand that she's really talking about, asking for, something other than the words she uses.

There are lots of reasons for this state of affairs, and certainly our not being fully aware of male/female trains of thought is in itself a source of confusion. We'll be looking at these other reasons (Chapter 2: *BARRIERS TO FULFILLMENT*) and eventually some ways to resolve the problems they cause.

For now, let's just be aware that within the dynamics of a male/female relationship, our differences can play havoc with communication. Yet these differences are quite complementary, and to some extent help define gender roles. Or, viewed from another angle, it can be said that our roles define and even require such differences in thinking.

Paula's Story:

Soon after our first Man-Woman Course, I can remember riding in a car with Leo and mentioning several things that I wanted. It was exciting to let my appetite run free and to express some ideas I had that might bring some additional fun into our life together. I can't even recall now exactly what they were, but I *do* remember that one desire had a strong priority and that I was positive it was clear to Leo what I most really wanted. After all, we'd been married a long time. We were close, and had just undergone a man-woman course. How could it be otherwise?

I can almost bet that the priority request was something to do with sex, but my memory fails me in this instance. I did double-check by asking Leo, rhetorically, if he knew what I most really wanted? To my amazement, and to our mutual amusement, he talked about the very last item discussed. When I reminded him of the item that was my top priority, he complained, "But we discussed that other thing fifteen minutes ago."

This was a prime experience of the global thinking and prioritizing that we women are best at, as opposed to the narrow (a woman's view) step-by-step, linear, male outlook. It was sobering for us both to realize that we, too, "fit the bill" for utilizing the different languages and thought of the sexes.

Leo's Assessment:

We were indeed in the car and Paula was talking about all kinds of things she wanted. They were different to be sure, but for me they were all one thing, i.e. requests, and my thoughts were geared to, that's right, getting the job done. My priority was with what I could handle first, easiest, and most quickly. Thereby I could shorten the list on my way to success. This was not at all geared to what Paula wanted most.

BARRIERS TO FULFILLMENT

2

We so deeply identify with our sexuality, that the biggest wins and losses are experienced in the bedroom. The rest is sublimation.

L.G.

The Flight From Pleasure

We are—all of us, at given times—running from pleasure. Our society is comprised of a pain oriented, pleasure avoiding majority. We understand and are comfortable with the phrase *Noble Suffering*, not *Noble Pleasure*. Yet, people won't admit this to others, much less themselves. They're willing to be the cause of pleasure, but don't like to take the rap for pain.

In most cases this tendency is so ingrained, so reflexive, that we passively accept it as the only reality—what we might call the "That's Life" syndrome. It's not as if we don't try to break out of these constraints. Indeed, at times our efforts to *get out there and party* may reach levels akin to a fun-seeking "feeding frenzy", becoming ends in themselves.

Our methods appear to be faulty and do not address our true needs. As if polarized like a magnet, we automatically spin away from real gratification and gravitate to the negative.

The expression "TGIF" (Thank Goodness It's Friday) is full of anticipation and hope. But come Monday morning, whatever little joys and pleasures, golden moments, that were mined from the stream of life on the weekend disappear like so much gold dust through our fingers.

This attitude to life and living is deeply ingrained and usually reflexive. We begin learning it from early childhood. The toddler, who on the contrary, gravitates towards pleasure and attempts to avoid pain, learns quickly that pleasure can be very dangerous, even potentially deadly. There, he or she is about to touch the so appealing, sparkling crystal vase, an act coupled with a terrifying parental shriek, of "Stop! Don't touch!" Thus pleasure is quickly and deeply equated with danger.

It doesn't stop with the vase. It's important to make this point because our frequent automatic avoidance of pleasure can really, at times, get in the way of our happiness.

Nowhere is this attitude more intense and detrimental than in the areas of sexuality and sensuality. This is not a moral judgment. This is merely a description of one mental mechanism that operates to thwart our happiness.

The repression of sexual pleasure in Western culture has its origins in the 2nd century, when sensuality became identified as the antithesis of spirituality. Uncontrolled passion, even in marriage, was seen as dangerous and destructive. Physical pleasure was seen to depress spiritual growth. Sexual desire evidenced a fall from religious grace.

Certainly through the ages the suppression of the pursuit of pleasure was coupled with severe religious pressures and was probably necessary in the service of simple survival, the daily struggle for food and shelter. Through subsequent periods—for reasons both political and religious—most European-based Western civilizations have found it convenient to support the continuance of these beliefs. For whatever reason, we carry the legacy of these restrictions and inhibitions.

We're not forgetting, in this context, the sexual revolution and "ME" generation of the sixties and seventies. All that frenzied self-indulgence was played with losing rules of the game, leaving most of those who played it frustrated, confused, and seeking that more desirable environment of commitment and true caring.

The next time you wind up not having a good time, whatever the importance of the given situation, do ask to what extent were you avoiding having fun!

Of course there are all kinds of reasons people conjure up to feel they don't deserve things. We could fill a book with them. For example: How often have you, just on the heels of having had a great time or receiving just what you wanted, been confronted with an opportunity to have more pleasure and say to yourself "No, I don't really need that"? It's kind of a post-pleasure response—as if you've already gotten yours and you don't deserve more pleasure so soon again. We are not comfortable with "too much" pleasure!

There are also times when denying ourselves pleasure is not preceded by anything special. For example: You've bought something and you're just not completely happy with it. Rather than dumping, returning, or giving it away, you keep it with the self-imposed injunction that you *have to* use it. You mustn't waste things, after all, and anyway you deserve to suffer for your "mistakes".

Given our training from early childhood, pleasure tends to look unsafe. To complicate matters, the price for pleasure is enjoyment. We often don't feel worthy of this.

The only reason to refuse an offer is a fear of loss. Ask yourself—what am I afraid of? What am I going to lose?

Most of us, too often, will choose to go down from flat, rather than up; it's just a direction we're more comfortable with. It would be best to be aware of this tendency, recognize it and strive to get on the path of having more fun in our lives. This path, hopefully more and more traveled, will have immeasurable secondary gains in happiness and health.

Even though we (the authors) profess the need for

the pursuit of more pleasure in our lives, we also admit that curious human need to pay for it. Being charitable and helping others can really help dissipate any potential guilt associated with more pleasure, and possibly avoid the waiting-for-the-other-shoe-to-drop syndrome. Still, some of us will always seek to counter-balance the good in our lives with the bad. We will see to it one way or another. Our premise here is that we're all starting with a major deficit in the pleasure account. Payment into this account is well overdue.

Ego

The truth is—father doesn't always know best; he just thinks he does. That male ego, so necessary and so well designed to get the job done, at times goes overboard and creates problems. When this happens, it does because the man is out of his role in the man-woman game. We mean here that this problem occurs when he butts in and too actively concerns himself with the *what* of things, above and beyond the *how*, simply because he thinks he knows better.

When a woman wants something—whether it's an expensive (too expensive?) dress or dinner out or whatever, *that's* what she wants, plain and simple. So when a man (in his typical egocentric and practically oriented way) comes up with a more "reasonable", less expensive alternative, it just doesn't satisfy. An approximation doesn't work; it simply doesn't fit the bill.

Of course, she'll go along with it, usually; she's used to not getting her way in such things. But she won't really be happy about it. The potential for an exciting, fun-filled and gratifying situation is lost again, lying beaten at the feet of male machismo. But, after all, he knew best!

Remember winning at this game is not a question of domination or surrender, but all parties winning. A guy really has to bite the bullet here. Spending some of that abundant ego of his is more than worth it! Admitting to this, a man might ask at this point "O.K., but when do I get mine?" The answer is that in a very real way he gets his when she gets what she wants! By giving her what she wants graciously and lovingly (not grudgingly) he wins and wins big! Grudgingly, here, doesn't refer to a guy grumbling about doing a job. He sometimes does this to get started. It's sort of like starting his production engine, and having to overcome some inertia. After all he doesn't want to fail.

There's lots of gratification in doing a job well, but one of the greatest pleasures is for a man to see that big smile and light in his woman's eyes. It benefits a man many times over if he can go along with a woman's goals, even if he feels he *can't* or it's some sort of issue with him. She may change her mind well before he reaches the actual stages of production. But more importantly, his going along, supporting her wishes, may be what she really wants. There's little sweeter to a woman's ears than her man's attention on her goals and his sincere pursuit of them.

All throughout this process, and well before the final stages of production, the man will be winning. It's also true that when a woman is gratified by her man's response to her desires, not only will her requests become more accurate, but he will receive all kinds of additional pleasures from her—not as pay backs, but as a result of her surplus of pleasure and happiness. This really happens and it feels wonderful.

Remember, as we mentioned earlier, this is a union of aliens not allies. Gratification is its own reward. Attaching bills or conditions as adjuncts to fulfilling a request significantly dissipates the pleasure in realizing the goal.

A woman's failure to get what she really wants from her man can result in a number of different counter-productive behaviors on her part. She may be more actively aggressive beyond the *what*, and get into the *how* of things in her attempt to attain her goal(s). This, in turn, can be very bruising to a man's ego, a losing scenario.

She may, on the other hand, continue to suppress her ego and appetite(s), something she has done throughout her life. In this very common maneuver, she just puts up with it; but you can be sure there's a bill to pay for this sometime down the line. Something will be turned inward, something will be withheld. The response may be overt and follow quickly on the heels of disappointment or, more often, subtle and quietly smoldering, that much more fuel for some future repelling eruption or negative response ("not tonight, dear . . .").

Or she may, from fear of asking for *too* much, ask for much less than might have been. There's really no great joy or adventure in this common female ploy. Let's call it *Ordering Short* in the man-woman game. It's superficially safe, but relatively empty. This, too, will be added to the tab. Why not go for more?

Failing is not losing! Losing is not being willing to fail, i.e. not being willing to take that chance, the plunge, and play the game for all it's worth. *Carpe diem* (seize the day)!

Leo:

It's very difficult for a man to understand the importance of giving to his woman without reservation. I ought to know! I've been there! My ego had supplied me with heavy blinders, restricting my view of reality. So like a work horse methodically plodding toward a misconceived goal, I saw nothing but the end point, not even realizing that it was off-center.

In general, the greater the price of something, whether it be an object or an experience, the more valuable it is for a woman. This has nothing to do with imposed value judgments of right and wrong; it's just the way things are! Consequently, good choices often cost a lot up front. Yet they are good, simply because they have big pay-offs further down the line. Poor choices, cheap thrills, may cost little to get into, but may cause damage and are hard to get out of.

I've always enjoyed buying Paula things, especially on special occasions. Any guy wants to please his gal in this way. This is a relatively easy way to win—or so it would seem.

I was a great fan of zirconia and other well-produced faux jewelry in general. To be sure, they have their places—they look pretty and oh those reasonable prices! Yet, ultimately they're no substitute for the real thing. On the other hand, I thought a guy has got to be crazy to spend so much money when there were cheaper alternatives which looked so much alike.

After getting more in step with the reality of the man-woman game however, I got a little crazy (like a fox) and finally decided to buy Paula (with her help in choosing such) a diamond ring. It certainly was a new me indeed—throwing caution (money) to the wind.

As soon as I made that decision, the fun began. First the excitement, and then you should have seen all the fun this generated for us both in shopping around for just the right ring. We looked at different styles and stone sizes. Our anticipation and excitement grew, knowing that at any moment our "dream ring" might appear. We finally wound up, many weeks and exciting episodes later, with a major diamond importer to choose loose stones to make up a ring of our own design.

Out-doing myself, I opted for the more perfect and

considerably more expensive stones from a plethora of lovely choices. I was amazed at how painless it was to spend more. Best of all, the glow in Paula's eyes outshone the diamonds.

She felt so happy and gratified by it all, and I felt triumphant by my great win with her. I spent a lot of money, a little ego, and it was all so perfect! Even today, I catch her smiling, admiring her ring as the light dances with it on her finger. I just keep winning with it.

It's so obvious that any substitute would have been a source of potential and perpetual loss. 

Money is only a tool which can be converted into experiences. Some experiences are priceless.

A woman's happiness is the true guide to the success of a relationship and sets the ceiling to how much happiness is available to the man. That's the bottom line!

Paula:

We were at an art show and had come upon a piece of sculpture of which I, especially, became enamored. Leo liked it too, and we kept coming back to take another look. My unwritten "want list" did include a piece of sculpture for our living room. We studied it over several hours debating its price and artistic merits until I realized that Leo would purchase it if I really wanted it! He actually asked me how much did I really want it, looking for that special gleam in my eye.

When I fully realized that I could actually own the piece of art, I backed off, aware that what I had wanted to experience had already occurred: I had wanted to experience my power as a woman—to experience the ability to get what I wanted from my man.

With that realization, I no longer needed to want the sculpture—at least not enough to pay the asking price, a sure give away for a lack of intention. The experience was wonderful and I made sure that Leo knew how much his attitude meant to me.

Miscommunication

Even assuming the best of intentions in the man-woman game, improper communication or the lack of communication will thwart the hardiest of efforts. We have already touched on the concepts of ordering short, codes, and different languages. Under this heading, we will play with examples of these, among other things.

Remember, a woman is often habituated to not getting what she wants. She spends mounds of energy sitting on her appetites, which she may even come to see as possibly too demanding. She is often afraid of failing as a result of her demands. She will set up barriers to her real desires, barriers which anticipate failure and become self-fulfilling, by asking for less.

It would therefore behoove men to listen very closely to their women, always anticipating this self-defeating mechanism, and the clouding effect of codes. Unfortunately, men frequently discount what women say (even though they rarely will say things without a purpose). Women don't often make "good" sense, according to men, because they fail in our collective mind to represent authority.

Let's see how some of these mechanisms might be played out:

Paula:

"I'm sick and tired of living in this place! It's a boring, small town. There's nothing to do. I'm sick of malls!"

(What Leo's hearing is that he's not winning with Paula and can't easily give her what she wants—short of getting a new job in a more exciting town—a very tall order!)

What is Paula really feeling? For one thing, she hasn't been getting what she wanted. On the surface she's looking for a change of scene, more motion, excitement, even travel to exciting places. Now people do enjoy traveling; so let's take her at her word. If her desire is to travel to a more exciting cultural climate, this want is just what Leo needs and wants to know. It presents an opportunity to produce something his lady genuinely wants.

However, travel is often another name for adventure and excitement in sensuality and sex. Of course, that exotic isle or big city can be fun by itself, but great love and sex are better still. If one isn't having that, the exotic isle is a poor substitute. Those shots on T.V. of Caribbean isles, palm trees and sunsets with the ocean lapping the shore aren't worth anything without that couple walking arm in arm along the beach, or those loving glances at the dinner table over Mai-tais.

What a woman wants is a date all the time, an exciting sexual life, which is getting better and better. She's really saying she wants more excitement and pleasure in the bedroom. Getting back to Leo's response:

Leo:

"What do you want me to do?"

(What he's really saying is: I'm making a good living; I'm providing a good life. So stop nagging me about something I can't change. I'm fed up with listening to you complain!)

A guy actually wants everything to be fine *right now*! It's hard enough to get him started on a quest to begin with. So finding him in the wrong up front is certainly a losing gambit!

Here is but another example of a woman wanting something very much, yet not making her position clear. She is not describing her actual needs to her man in a form which he can recognize. This is most often true when it comes to things sexual. So tied up are our identities and self-esteem with this aspect of our personalities, that we are very careful and reluctant to openly discuss our sexual needs with each other. Thus, in the above example, by finding things wrong and nothing right (including Leo) Paula assured failure in the communication process and in attaining her goal.

Sometimes it is not so much a question of miscommunication, but actually a total lack of communication that occurs. Certainly when it comes to sex, if there's any caring at all in the relationship, we are very conscious of how easily one's ego can be bruised by finding a partner inadequate sexually in any way. Most of us are often content to take what we get and let it go at that.

Man: "Was it good for you, honey?" (It was, wasn't it? *Wasn't* it?)
Woman: "Sure!" (As good as it's ever been: no big deal.)
Man: "It was for me too; it was great!" (Whew, I *am* really good, aren't I?)

And so the saga, the myth, continues: the man feeling a false sense of sexual accomplishment, and the woman, a lack of sexual fulfillment.

Paula:

I woke up with an unsettled feeling in my stomach. Something wasn't quite right with the world and I didn't know how to fix it. I kept reaching out to Leo, off and on, throughout the day, wanting him to fix it, to fix that not-quite-right feeling. Only I didn't tell him. I didn't know exactly what to tell him. I just hinted.

Somewhere I felt that it wouldn't take much effort or time or anything "big deal" on his part to fix it. Only I wasn't telling. Why? What was I afraid of?

What I feared was exactly what I ended up getting. Through my lack of clear communication, I got rejection (or my perception of a rejection). More importantly, my sense of a lack of rightness continued.

Things finally escalated to the point where I lost my temper. Becoming totally unattractive, I thus sealed my fate.

What I truly wanted was Leo's warmth, affection, love, his touch.

How could I train him to take note, when I'm especially fractious, and do the opposite of what he feels at that moment? A hug, an acknowledgement that I'm right and loved is what I most wanted. A peppering of those hugs and squeezes throughout the day, with some special time set aside *just for me* was what I called for. Yet I wanted him to give it without my request. I *so* wanted him to *know* without my telling him. That was my right, after all, wasn't it?

Leo:

It happens! Paula would want, need something and for whatever reason—her not even knowing exactly what it was herself, or perhaps her demanding that I already know the answer without her telling me—she would or could not communicate in concrete terms her needs to me. Or she would beat around the bush and confuse me. In either case I was handicapped and heading for a fall. A man can't give his woman something she wants when he doesn't know what it is.

Even if she was confused and my cuddling her would have helped, she acted in ways to short circuit such a response. Her asking, at least, for that would have helped, instead of complaining all day!

Once he is aware of this particular game and its pitfalls, a guy, instead of feeling himself a loser by not exactly identifying the problem and solving it, could try putting his attention on her—some high grade affection. This could, at times, cut the potential blowout off at the pass.

One major source of bitchiness in women is unrelieved sexual tension. When a lot of this tension builds in many of us, it serves as the underlying source of many cracks in the surface of our relationships. We will address this form of tension again in Chapter 3.

Forms of Castration

Although a woman generally lives in an environment of scarcity where she often doesn't get what she wants, can't say what she wants, or feel what she wants, her being instrumental in her man (or a man) losing, need not always be out of meanness or revenge.

Any time a man can't produce that something for which there is a demand, for whatever reason, there is a danger of him feeling emasculated. This being the case, miscommunication or the lack of communication by a woman is, in a way, itself castrating. This is so because poor communication makes it very difficult or even prevents a man from properly responding to the pressure to produce. He'll usually respond, but he'll get it wrong. His production will be faulty.

Ordering short, as a form of miscommunication, may also have an unintended castrating effect in a slightly different way. It fuels a man's fears of inadequate production, of not making the grade. This is so because by settling for less, she is telling him, indirectly, that she believes him incapable of getting the real job done.

Of course, a woman may more actively pursue a vengeful course in which she chronically trains her man with such losses. Men will have different tolerances to such treatment, and usually can take a lot. Yet, sooner or later limits will be reached, at which point he'll just withdraw from the relationship. (Rhett Butler's famous parting words to Scarlett—"Frankly my dear, I don't give a damn," underscores this endpoint.)

At times, however, a woman will (covertly) find her man wrong just to keep him off-balance in an attempt to get control of the relationship. She may find him wrong by openly attacking him, or she may be more subtle in her approach (but no less devastating, if less dramatic) with "you're great, but this isn't right and you can't help it".

Another, less direct, tactic she may employ is demanding the impossible. This is accomplished by being too vague or cryptic (as discussed earlier) in her demands, so that there's no way he can deliver. Or, she may in fact just ask him to do the impossible: for example, to get her a glass of water when they're in the middle of the desert.

In instances such as these, it's really up to the guy to call her on these actions. He needs to call it as he sees it. In spite of the potential confrontation, she will think even less of him if he doesn't, and things could get worse. (If I can't even get his attention by punching him, what should I do next?)

Remember, all these castrating ploys are roadblocks to happiness. A woman needs to ask herself if she'd rather consume a dish of revenge rather than a meal of pleasure. For although revenge may be sweet, its sweetness disappears like so much cotton candy along with the whole merry-go-round ride. There's no gold ring here, for when she makes her man lose, she ultimately loses too. Thus it would behoove her to grab onto something positive in the relationship, in him, and pull up from there. It is a long way down and the winds of loneliness are very cold. And even though she may not think that he's the best transportation, he'll still get her somewhere, which is better than nowhere.

A woman has direct control of the way her man looks. She can polish him with wins and make him shine, looking and feeling like new. Or she can kick him with losses, leaving him scratched, dirty and dented and barely able to go the distance. It's your ride ladies—YOU CHOOSE!

Trust and Betrayal

Paula:

At one point in my musical career, I made the difficult choice to go for a doctorate degree. I subsequently and painfully changed my mind because there was too great a clash of personalities and philosophies between an important master teacher in the program and myself. It seems grossly exaggerated to me now, but back then I felt like a failure, so deeply tied up was my identity with my music. I felt quite vulnerable, hardly knowing which way to turn.

Thus, I thought my prayers answered when my closest friend volunteered an introduction to her teacher. He was someone I wanted to study with. However as he was difficult to contact by phone or letter, introductions were hard to come by.

Everything was all set up. We were to go together. I could get introduced, and what would follow would be a first lesson. It was a bright ray of sunshine in an area of my life which had appeared dark for some months.

Just prior to the appointed meeting time, however, my friend called to say that she hadn't been able to exercise regularly enough. She felt she absolutely had to take a class during the same period. Otherwise she would be out of sorts.

I was speechless, crushed. I felt confused and rejected. How could she have done this to me? At a time when I was low and in need of a helping hand, my best friend had dealt what to me felt like a crippling blow. My pain and depression were severe, at least for awhile. Our relationship changed for many years to one that was more distant, superficial, and for me lacking in trust.

Today I can see she couldn't possibly have understood the significance of what took place between us then. These were expectations, and this, a particular event that held a private significance in my life story. Yet that was not so obvious to her.

All of us have felt "betrayed" at some time, in some way. The sense of betrayal is a very personal one and frequently may have little if anything to do with the motivation of the other person.

The ultimate and heavy price for betrayal is at best a weakening of ties between us; at worst, and more frequently, a disruption of those ties. These nurturing cords of interpersonal relationships may be delicate with gossamer-like connections or thick and deeply rooted. The pain and loss caused by the disruption of such ties is directly proportional to their strength, as parts of us are torn when deep bonds pull away.

Granted, at times such as these it is often too painful to renew such torn relationships, not to mention there being the presence of a pervasive sense of hurt pride and self-righteousness. What really happens when such things occur, and to what extent are we responsible ourselves?

Without trust there would be no betrayal.

There is a great harvest of pleasure and joy awaiting those who plant the seeds of intimacy—being open to and with others. However, the sense or the fear of betrayal can tear people apart and keep them apart. We are reluctant to expose ourselves, our vulnerabilities, and keep large parts of ourselves separate from each other.

Without the expectation that someone is going to, or is *supposed to* act in a certain way, there would be no betrayal. Betrayal by its very definition means that we find another's behavior to be wrong. Finding everyone's behavior as right prevents the evolution of betrayal.

People betray us when they don't act in ways we think they *should.* Either they just don't care, or have different value systems (ways of looking at things), or miscommunication has occurred. In fact, we can say that the more vulnerable we are in a given situation, the more likely is miscommunication apt to occur. Trust is a risky maneuver and we are less likely to place it fully when we have a lot on the line and much to lose. This is a mechanism much akin to ordering short.

We may think we have clearly communicated a need, or subconsciously expect the other person to know us well enough to be sensitive to our vulnerabilities.

Knowing of the particular mechanism leading to a given episode of betrayal may dictate our later less judgmental response to it. The initial response is usually painful and blinding. Later responses may be: 1) Finding the other person right (accepting them for who they are) and thereby diffusing any sense of betrayal; 2) Changing the other person's position (getting them into agreement with your viewpoint); 3) Clearing up any perceived miscommunication; 4) Changing your assessment of them (i.e. they were not the people you thought they were) and adjusting accordingly; 5) Ending the relationship.

Of course there are countless examples and levels through which one may experience being betrayed, but whatever the scenario, the mechanisms are quite similar and begin with the presence of trust in place, whether well-founded or flippantly endowed. Trust is a set-up for betrayal. In a real sense, one betrays one's self. We trust others to act "fairly", hold values similar to ours, or to do the "right thing". But these are all value judgments very much in the mind and heart of the beholder.

People are who they are, and if we know them and accept them, we can't then be betrayed by them. It's really our responsibility to get to know others, assuming we want a relationship with them. During this initial phase of all relationships, a healthy dose of skepticism and an awareness of the varied value systems people embrace in their own particular way should stem the tide of potential disappointment, as we discover what we may consider defects in their mantle of perfection, based on our value judgments and prejudices.

After this period of discovery and acclimation, if we *accept them for who they are* (their uniqueness), how can people disappoint us or surprise us with their behavior? If I'm a stickler for punctuality and one of my friends isn't, why should I get annoyed at him or her for keeping me waiting, after I know that they usually arrive late at a given rendezvous? Why complain about getting wet, when I chose to stand in the rain?

Likewise, being on time is the way I am. So if I come on time to your dinner party, and you're far from ready because you believe people are supposed to come late to such affairs, please don't be annoyed with me. It's just the way I am, remember?

If you create a rule that doesn't fit the other person, then the relationship is headed for a fall. If you want to be trusted by someone, you need only to increase your predictability in relation to them through knowing their value judgments and doing what they expect of you.

Paula and Leo:

Let's end this section on a positive note, one which clearly demonstrates the realities and principles of knowing others and finding them right.

Our son went off to college last year. He had been so anxious to do this that he gained early admission and a partial academic scholarship to boot, accomplishments certainly indicative of academic potential. Obviously, he had the ability to do well, assuming the proper motivation. We were aware, however, that his commitment to academics was questionable at the time. Yet we decided not to stand in his way, and hope for the best. In the end, he not only lost his scholarship, but did very poorly.

In the past, we would have felt betrayed by him, very hurt and angry (typical responses, which usually make things much worse). We had, after all, given him much emotional and financial support in this venture. Furthermore, we knew he had the ability to succeed. We wanted him so to excel in areas in which we took pride, and in those we felt so strongly were important for his future.

Well, we were disappointed, if not too surprised. We found him right in the sense that we understood his lack of interest in academics at this time, and had by his choice of action made it very clear that he wanted out of college (at least for now). We even commended his bravery in consequently opting for the tougher, hard knocks choice of getting a job and working, rather than choosing the insulated and relatively comfortable environment of a college campus.

He had expected a blow-out, and his surprise at our calm attitude was quite amusing. There was no betrayal, no anger, no shouting, no accusations or pain—but a deeper understanding and appreciation of each other, on both sides. Perhaps he'll return to college some day, but we will love him no less whatever his choices.

Rights and Anger

Anger is aggression coupled with the intention to destroy something. It may be automatic and quick to surface, or ominously smouldering. It is often seductive, cloaked in self-righteousness. To be sure, when it surfaces damage will be done—whether external to its source, internal (within ourselves), or both. In this latter connection, medicine is rightly paying more attention to the mind-body connection and its influence on the production of physical disease.

Paula's Story:

It's amazing how we can change. I can't remember exactly when the following occurred, but it was quite a few years ago.

I wanted Leo's attention, but not just any kind. It's obvious to me now that I must have actually wanted some intense affection or hot love-making. It was one of those lazy Sundays and Leo was watching a football game (ever been in a situation like this?). I sat down beside him, feebly trying to make my presence felt. I wanted all of his attention on me. Yet at the same time, I knew that he was very much enjoying the ball game, as he attempted to share his excitement about "that great pass" telling me to "look at that catch on the replay". It was all football and I was getting frustrated. So I got up and changed into something sexy and more revealing, hoping to draw his focus on me. No luck! He even seemed somewhat annoyed by the intrusion and now I began fuming inside, feeling rejected and really getting angry. It was building and building with each minute of that silly game. I guess he sensed this because he finally asked me what the problem was. I exploded, letting him have it with a torrent of how he *never* paid enough attention to me, how bored I was, and how selfish he was. My eyes flashed, my pulse raced and neither of us was loving toward the other. Leo just continued to watch the game. I felt so agitated that I nearly ran out for a drive in the car, to get away, anything. Yet I fought the impulse, knowing that I was an accident waiting to happen.

Our moods lasted until morning. No sex, no fun of any kind—just tension and stress. Anger certainly got me what I had wanted, didn't it!

Leo's Revelation:

Here is a shining example of how I really messed up. That's right. *I* did! You men may say—now wait a minute—we have a right to watch our football game! Well, yes and no—just like you, I really didn't know any better.

Here was the love of my life, the person who meant (and still means) more to me than anything, opening herself up to me, giving me the opportunity to give her great pleasure—an act that would have been extremely gratifying for me, much more than a game on T.V. In addition, we need hardly mention all the damage resulting from my not putting my attention where it really belonged—on her.

At least some acknowledgment was called for. Some arrangement could and should have been made. This is especially critical, when our women openly call out for something!

What a dummy I was. Instead of delighted, I was actually annoyed, just feeling pressure from Paula and wanting to see that game. Couldn't she wait?

Perhaps, who knows, but she certainly wasn't getting any positive responses from me—just rejection. (Why does it have to be now? Can't I have a couple of hours of peace/freedom?)

A little understanding, some affection may have helped, but no! I had a right to watch the game. I sensed her annoyance, and even though I suspected her need, I couldn't help asking what her problem was. After all, we guys can't quite shirk our need to fix things.

Then I got it with both barrels. That did it!

I know now that even when her anger spilled over at that moment, had I wanted to—chosen to—I might have turned things around. This is so because anger, while not quite the same, is still very akin to sexual arousal: fast pulse, increasing blood pressure, excitement and agitation, fast heavy breathing.

Something disarming like "Oh, come on honey, you look so sexy. Give me a hug!" was worth a try. This should not come across as making light of the situation (something which would just cause more anger in her) but a genuine attempt to recognize her sexual tension and attractiveness with the intention to do something about it. But I was having none of that. I was buying into my own anger track.

We were like two runaway trains on the same track, heading on a collision course with its inevitable destructive outcome. That darn game really wasn't worth it! The rest of the day was lousy. We behaved very cooly to each other. I didn't get a good night's sleep either. What a mess! What could have been fulfillment for her and a triumph for me was a disaster instead!

Paula's Response:

There were a number of ways I could have behaved to have us both win. For instance, when I saw my initial hints weren't getting anywhere, I could have gotten Leo's focused attention during a break, expressed my needs clearly, and given him the option to wait until after the game, if that continued to keep his interest. With his acknowledgment of this, then into the bedroom with me to put on my sexiest outfit. Then I could rejoin him (*not* to put the pressure on, but to perhaps tease a little, show some interest in watching the game, and to enjoy the anticipation of a post-game sexual celebration.) I would have savored the waiting.

It's a woman's role to be attractive, to make it attractive for her man to produce for her. Just being demanding doesn't hack it! The wonderful communication and deep caring Leo and I enjoy usually results in our both winning these days.

Anger is a counter-productive force which often hurts and keeps us apart. Victor Baranco has referred to anger as "a wound waiting to happen". This emotion is part of us. It can't be ignored, but we do have a choice of how we deal with it.

Where does this anger come from? It evolves through one's perception that one or more personal "rights" have been violated. Think of a time when you were angry and try to remember how you were "wronged". What right of yours was infringed, as you perceived it?

A right is a "guarantee" that something bad won't happen. But bad things do happen, even to nice people. We all have the right to life, liberty and the pursuit of happiness, all destroyed in an instant if our lives are taken. What does it all mean?

Our rights are really just a pseudo shield and merely serve as vehicles for potential retribution after their infringement. They are actually preventative only to the extent that we allow them to be, whether through conscience or from fear of retribution. They are truly paper treaties between us, which at any moment may be torn asunder.

What one perceives as a violation is the key here. We have a choice. Anger very much gets in the way of the pursuit of our pleasure. It is an excellent tool which may dig a pit of unhappiness too deep to escape from. If it's happiness we're after, it would be best to get out of this violation—anger—revenge cycle.

Of course one needs to deal with this destructive emotion. How we do so is critical. Venting it or turning it inward (holding it) causes damage, overt or insidious. Review the "right" you thought was violated and ask yourself if you want pleasure or revenge? Is the retribution worth it? What's the price for such?

What to do? You can change your mind! One thing you may consider is acknowledging your anger, just admitting that you're angry and then deliberately deciding to put it aside for the moment. Put it where it really belongs—with the garbage in a garbage can, outside.

If you do this and get back into your relationship in a more positive loving way, you'll be surprised how often that garbage can will have been mysteriously emptied by morning. If on the other hand you take the anger to bed with you, it will just stink everything up, as garbage tends to do.

A very disarming way to handle another person's anger is to get into agreement with it. Agreement is control. It's like turning into a skid and being able to gain control and then straightening out. The following example will illustrate this principle.

Leo:

I must have had my mind on other things when, at the last moment, I turned my car sharply left into the left lane. I wanted access to the small shopping center a few yards further down the road. A loud blast from the horn of a car in that lane really startled me. I hadn't seen him. No harm was done. No collision. It was just one of those close calls.

I pulled into the small shopping center and parked. To my surprise and discomfort, the car I had cut off pulled in and parked there as well. A driver literally jumped out of that car and came towards me flushed with anger. I had a sinking feeling. This was scary. He was yelling at me, very angry and menacing.

I slowly looked his way, quietly apologized and found him right for being angry. After all, I had cut him off, even though I privately thought him a little crazy to react the way he had.

Guess I was really lucky he didn't have a weapon. Where would my rights have been then?

My non-confrontational stance and agreement at once—and quite remarkably—took the wind out of his sails. He was reduced to speechlessness, finally muttering something like "just watch out". It was over quickly and no one got hurt.

What would have happened had I lost my cool and been confrontational? I'm really happy I didn't find out.

Jealousy

In any relationship in which the participants have evolved a special sense of belonging to one another, real or perceived, jealousy may arise if one experiences a sense of *being excluded in a sexual context.*[1] We have all experienced this emotion at one time or another.

In proper amounts and appropriate contexts, it is a normal and natural feeling. We can even say that the lack of such a response by one partner in a given relationship, in charged-up situations, probably wouldn't be appreciated at all by the other. For even though it carries seeds of potential destruction, jealousy at least signals that the other partner cares.

We can easily conjure up scenarios in which jealousy can be readily evoked. For example, a dinner party at which the wife (or husband) seems to be spending a lot of time with a member of the opposite sex may bring out such jealous feelings in the "excluded" spouse.

Whatever the underlying mechanisms, the resultant searing common emotion of jealousy is the same. We must remember that men and women are often trained with losses, starting in childhood (Will little Johnny or Janie ever get it right?). Men are very vulnerable in areas of production, especially sexual. There's really lots of emotional charge here.

Any perceived threat to his or her significant relationship, any challenge, is bound to play into an individual's potential fears of inadequacy and loss. Also if an individual has his or her own fantasies of dangerous liaisons outside of the significant pairing, there is a possibility of projecting such feelings onto the partner. [I feel these things; why shouldn't she (or he)? Can I trust her (or him)?] Also, let's remember that most women are starved for sex and attention, or certainly not getting what they could in this very important area of their lives. In such circumstances, without a surplus of sexual gratification and atten-

[1]Any interchange, emotional, verbal or physical between a man and a woman is within the realm of sexual context. We are defined by our differences, our sexuality.

tion, if they perceive their man even having eyes for someone else, they're bound to feel jealous. (If I'm not getting enough, he's not going to waste his attention on someone else, even for a moment!)

Trust also plays a role here. For if trust is firmly in place, a little touch of jealousy can be used in a positive way. For example, you're aware that your man is really turned on to that sexy woman in the short dress and heels walking by. You could feel jealous and even get angry—downhill all the way. Or, knowing that he would not act on such arousal with strangers, you could possibly redirect such feelings (the arousal) towards you—use it for yourself. Snuggle up, perhaps talk about the good time you're going to have together, later. Buy that sexy piece of lingerie. Oh, the joys of anticipation! It can really be fun.

So what have we been talking about, and how can we handle such emotions? As individuals, the amount and frequency of jealousy we experience along with its potential to do damage will vary significantly among us according to the situation. But let's remember that jealousy is *sexually charged emotion* coupled with the feeling of *being excluded*. The key here is a very open and active communication between partners and inclusion! If someone truly doesn't feel left out they won't feel jealous. There will be nothing to be jealous about. That's a sure way to keep someone else from feeling jealous. Failing this, i.e. if your partner is apparently "excluding" you, talking with someone else, dancing with someone else, you may try communicating, non-confrontationally, with him (or her) when an opening arises. Or you may decide not to buy into your jealousy and decide to have a good time yourself.[2]

[2]We're not necessarily talking about fighting fire with fire here, i.e. making your partner jealous by openly flirting with a member of the opposite sex.

Having lots of fun acts like a true magnet and you may discover all kinds of people, including your partner, by your side. This would be akin to overcoming our feeling jealous by being *at cause*. You may keep yourself from having jealous feelings by being in the driver's seat, that is, being in control, being the *cause* for what is going on.

Leo:

I was, as you'll remember, feeling quite threatened by all this material up front (ref. *First Impressions, His*). I was (and still am) very possessive of Paula and was worried that I couldn't give her all she wanted, sexually or otherwise. Perhaps someone else ultimately would. Throughout this period, situations arose which caused me to feel jealous. But the more I came to understand the nature of my jealousy, the more it waned. I realized that I was bringing this new knowledge and experience to Paula, that I was not being excluded, and that I was making it happen. We always worked through problems with good communication, always including one another. We've learned a lot and are enjoying life and each other so much more as a result. We've never bought into something that was so well worth the price.

Of course, all this does not mean that I am immune from feelings of jealousy. It does mean that I less frequently and less deeply buy into such emotions. Consequently such feelings are more easily accepted, understood, and less damaging—a much better place to be.

Myth of Insatiability

In the service of underscoring what is, we must reiterate that the vast majority of women are far from gratified sexually and emotionally. It is this reality that underlies their reluctance to admit or even consider the possibility that they may have the capacity to be satiated. Many have never experienced such fullness. They are therefore hard pressed to honestly say that they've had enough. Living in a state of scarcity causes us to want more or to give up and to want practically nothing. And the more we get, the more we demand. Women may consequently come across as insatiable creatures, a myth that is perpetuated by their lack of gratification. They have been led to and allow themselves to believe that what they're getting is what there is to be had—period. They are in reality selling themselves short. There is a lot more to be had!

Those who are starting out on this incredible road to sexual discovery and gratification are like hungry kids in a candy shop, not about to leave and grabbing all they possibly can. This is a situation indicative of not being full. But with true gratification comes satiation and fullness. Such levels of complete fulfillment are so unusual for most of us that we will hardly recognize them at first. We may be afraid even to admit them, as if admitting such would stop the flow of all this joy and pleasure.

As a matter of fact, it does become important for a woman to recognize her fullness, relax and just enjoy her consumption. If she doesn't do this and keeps on calling for more and more, she may get "indigestion"—whether it be emotional or sexual. That is, it just won't feel right or be gratifying at that point. Playing this gimme, gimme game and not recognizing her fullness will also misuse what her man is producing—something he'll feel and won't appreciate.

Since excess production can turn into garbage, it'll be wasted. It's a little like what happens after that luscious meal you've just finished. You're completely satisfied and full; but when it comes to dessert, you just can't say no to that delicious, rich chocolate cake on the pastry tray. You want it and you can't really eat it all. Your eyes are bigger than your stomach. Perhaps someone at your table helps, or most of it just goes to waste, which is certainly less satisfying.

Remember too that when a woman is truly sexually gratified and full there is the potential for her fullness to overflow into a very strong desire to give her man pleasure. This is not a pay back, tit for tat, 50-50 deal. It is overflow, surplus and very powerful in its ability to create pleasure, which is more gratifying than conventional approaches.

Paula:

We were on vacation in Florida. There was no pressure to rush to see the sights. Sleeping late, relaxing, enjoying the beauty and sounds of the ocean and skies were the agenda. A welcome change and release.

I was feeling hot, turned on sexually. I wanted to be done[3] constantly, taking breaks only for a nap or a walk on the beach or a good meal out. Leo and I had made out 3 times that day—each time superb in its own right. I was filled with wonder at what I was experiencing, sensually and sexually, my orgasms were so extended and intense. Just indescribable.

What a joy to be alive! I wanted to continue going up and up—so much so that I ignored some tell-tale signs of fullness (like the chocolate cake, I wanted it just with my eyes). Even Leo seemed to be reflecting my inability to acknowledge my fullness (I suppose he felt some pressure and sensed it was misguided) as he seemed a bit irritable, quite unlike him these days. Of course at the time neither of us were fully aware of

[3]Briefly, getting done is being brought to sexual orgasm by clitoral stimulation (see SEX in Chapter 3).

what was going on. I guess I just wanted the intensity and excitement to continue. It was late and I put something sexy on and got into bed; I wasn't aware of my fullness sexually at that moment.

A sexy outfit is a call for some action, and Leo began playing with me. But what had during the day been so wonderful was instead too sensitive, at times even unpleasant!

I asked him to be lighter with his touch, to use more lubrication, a request with which he complied. This helped, but didn't create the ecstasy I had anticipated.

He was becoming bored and sleepy. I asked for a few more strokes and enjoyed them to the fullest. He stopped, just applying pressure to my perineum to bring me down[4]. He seemed relieved.

Yet, I didn't feel quite right. I was a little upset at the course of events, until I leaned over and touched him. Something suddenly happened. I rubbed his back, which felt so good to my fingertips. I was getting excited and wanted so to give him great pleasure. So that was it! I had been full, my body spent, but hadn't recognized it. This was overflow, and I had wanted, needed something, but had ordered wrong. In the right direction (my bringing him to orgasm) things really took off; he had a great time and I enjoyed every moment of my passion and joy, such that I experienced fulfillment again.

[4]Pressure, especially on the perineum, feels good and dissipates any discomfort and tension which would result from the abrupt cessation of all activity following orgasm, or any state of sexual excitation. This is accomplished by applying the palm of one's hand firmly to the area which includes the clitoris, vaginal opening, and the zone between the vagina and anus.

ROLES AND DYNAMICS IN THE MAN-WOMAN GAME

3

That man is greatly empowered and gratified who, without doubt, fully satisfies his woman sexually. This act surpasses any Olympian feat of strength in his unending search for acknowledgment of his masculinity.

L.G.

Call—Response—Production—Consumption—Acknowledgement

Like all the examples in this book, this really happened:

After trying numerous ways of introducing the principles of this chapter we were at an impasse.

Paula:

"Honey, we need to start it off with some actual quotes—make it real, something people will relate to."

Leo:

"I know that would be best, but I don't want it to sound dinky, like some bad commercial: *girl wants something—boy gets it—they ride off into sunset.* See? Dinky! How do you put that into words, into a scenario that won't seem childish?"

Paula:

"I don't think it's dinky or childish."

Leo:

"Oh, yes it is!"

And so we see just another typical episode in this man-woman saga—an interchange demonstrating how things women want or feel are sometimes at odds with a man's perceptions. Oh, what fun it is!

Darn, impasse again!

(10 minutes later) *Leo:*

"Wow! But this is what it's all about. Writing this book is in fact a perfect example. I have wanted and enjoyed the writing (production) of this book (not without lots of Paula's help and approval). Yet I'm really doing it because she wants it. I'm producing it for *her*".

If you stop to think about it, so many things over the ages have been produced by men for their women, whether they were mothers, wives, lovers or idealized significant others (or possibly God).

When a man produces just what his woman wants, on schedule, she is fulfilled and he is very gratified in his accomplishment and in the pleasure he has given her. Try to remember how you felt when you surprised your lady with the "perfect" gift, or special dinner out, or weekend away that was such fun. There's nothing like that smile on her face, that light in her eyes, qualities that make you feel on top of the world.

Within the context of the man-woman game, the most fun and gratifying relationships happen when men and women play out their most appropriate roles. Now we are all good actors in this game, and are able and can play any role we wish, regardless of gender. This is fine as long as our major roles are not short-changed. That is, there are basic and intrinsic needs for men and women which, if not substantially met through the use of our appropriate roles, prevent our fulfillment. Put very simply, the major role of the man is that of producer (the how, the means, the deliverer); for the woman, it's the initiator and consumer (the what).

A complete cycle consists of call—response—production—consumption and finally, acknowledgement.

The woman is gratified and fulfilled when she consumes what has been produced for her. The man actually has two shots at being gratified: once while he's producing, and secondly when he's acknowledged by his partner following her consumption. To further and more fully understand these dynamics, let's get into more detail.

The play begins because a woman has appetites, for all kinds of things. Of course men (to a lesser degree) have appetites too, but for the woman it's part of her soul. At some point, then, when her appetite, her need, exceeds her fear of being turned down (being rejected), she'll send some signal, put out a call—overt or subtle.

Now, in general, guys like to be just left alone to "do their own thing", whether it be watching a game, being with the boys, tinkering with their cars or whatever—you know, the manly pursuits—"man things". In a sense these activities and hobbies are males' ways of feeding their own appetites, although at times they are production oriented. It's just that a woman enjoys and has a greater capacity for consumption than a man, who is much more of a production junkie.

Men want (if you remember) everything to be fine *now*! Yet they are often awakened from such blissful masculine slumbers by the "call of the wild". Their deep seated nature, their need to produce, to win, to be successful makes it often impossible to resist the challenge of picking up their lady's gauntlet—her call for something. A man can hardly ignore a fair damsel in distress, real or imagined. To be sure, there is usually some resistance on the part of our gallant knight to don his armour, take up his lance, mount his white steed and ride off to slay the dragon. After all, at some level he just doesn't want to be bothered. But more importantly, with a challenge comes the danger, the possibility of failure, something no man wants to face—being a loser.

He won't admit it, even to himself, but without the challenge it would all be a bore and no fun at all. In fact he may even unknowingly inflate the danger by his resistance; for the tougher the challenge, the bigger the accomplishment, the greater the rewards. There are exceptions, but in general a man tends to set his sights at a level just below that which he thinks he can accomplish, as this to his mind assures success and prevents failure. He's often uncomfortable with taking chances.

Fortunately or unfortunately for him, his fair lady often demands much more of him. This is best for both of them, because this whole game would be no fun without the drama, without the true challenge. Thus through her demands she offers him the opportunity to accomplish more than he thought himself capable of, a wonderful experience indeed.

It's great to be a hero and slay that dragon! The very fact that she even wants him to do it to some extent empowers him, gives him the confidence to get the job done. The stronger her appetite, the greater the energy and the more potentially empowering to him it is. There may be other reasons for his resistance. His grumbling may merely represent the turning on of his cold production engine. Often it just takes a little time to warm up and get started. With sophistication and genuine honesty in playing at the man-woman game, a guy in the know may resist his woman's call for something, if he senses that it is not genuine. He after all doesn't want to waste his production.

Of course he may resist or refuse to act, simply because he is what we would call a "hard head". That is, he is someone so self-centered, so me-first oriented and chauvinistic in his outlook that he doesn't care to respond appropriately. Such a lack of response needn't be across the board. Remember we all live in the same society with the same gender-based cultural paradigms, and most guys now and then may fall into this negative trap. However, if a given relationship is characterized by such hard-headedness and that's what she wants, it's her choice. Yet, as you can imagine, there's much greater happiness for sure in playing this game differently.

Alternatively, a man may refuse to respond because of his fear of loss. Beyond his fear of failing, there may be many other individual and personal fears at play here. He may feel there is something he knows or vaguely senses he will lose, and such thoughts are at the time too painful or threatening to overcome. This may evidence emotional/mental problems, which are beyond the scope of this book.

It's up to both parties in any relationship to get to know each other. As greater intimacy and honesty evolve, both partners can break through most male resistance, more than enough to gain a strong foothold in their climb to happiness. We are united behind truth, divided behind lies.

The important thing is for the man to take it on, to accept the challenge (not grudgingly, and without attached bills). Remember that a little grumbling is O.K. A man responding to a woman's call, in this context, is thrown into a production phase which gets him on the road to getting the job done. It's important to note that, if our knight pursues his goal with gusto and zest, even if he stumbles and falls, his lady will be there to pick him up, dust him off lovingly, and send him off again. A man gets a lot of gratification when he's producing.

It can get a little scary at times, but remember without the possibility of failure, there would be little excitement, no challenge, no pleasure in achievement and no potential for "heroism". What a bore it would be without these dynamics. Having fun often requires an element of instability, some risk; while production requires a strong element of stability and control. There are nuances here, dichotomies which set minds spinning and get the juices flowing. For women, life is valued on the experience, the fun of it; they're the pushers, initiators, the juice, the conduit for experiences both frightening and wondrous.

In most instances, the man is just driving along quietly at the speed limit, when all of a sudden his woman leans over and floors the gas pedal, and suddenly their lives are speeding wildly down that road.[5] Eventually he may be successful in applying the brakes, especially after she has had her fill of this exhilarating joyride and doesn't have her foot on the gas any more. In fact if the man goes full speed ahead without concern or resistance, she may be the one in due course to apply the brakes.

In reality, although there are some very exciting moments where we substantially break speed limits, most couples quite appropriately work in tandem such that gas and brakes (pressure and resistance) are shared and the right speeds are attained.

Leo:

If you'll remember I felt quite threatened by the More courses, the teachers and material. So when we planned and did go out to California to take some advanced courses and see what this community was

[5] We're reminded again of our friend Professor Higgins praising the calm and joys of bachelorhood which are totally disrupted when you "let a woman in your life!"

all about, this was unsettling to me to say the least. I was afraid things would happen I couldn't measure up to or control. I didn't want to fail. Consequently I didn't go gently into them—at times I went kicking and screaming. But I did it because of Paula. I knew she wanted this information very much. I sensed that being completely hard headed and refusing to give these things to her (a danger we men are prone to) could have ended in disaster. The smarter thing was to accept the challenge and go for it.

This was much smarter than I knew. What I eventually experienced was the most fun, the greatest adventures I've ever had. None of this (including the book you are reading) would have happened but for Paula.

A great example of what we've been talking about is the classic film *The African Queen*. Superficially stated, in this wonderful film Kathryn Hepburn pushes Humphrey Bogart to heroic acts while he grumbles all the way. See this film with these principles in mind—it's a classic in more ways than one.

During the production phase it can be very encouraging and stimulating for a woman to cheer her man on. A woman's approval is power. A woman will be very excited by her man's reaching for her goals, but excitement per se can't take the place of her approval of him for his position, even at this early stage of the cycle. As a matter of fact a man may feel that he's producing too much and may lose interest if he doesn't receive some approval at this stage.

Before we go any further, let's remind ourselves about ordering short. It's up to the man (even with all of his trepidation) to really put his attention on her, to question her orders and carefully look for that special gleam, that flash, that twinkle in her eyes broadcasting her true goals. He's like a cook looking at orders she hangs on one of those turning wheels. There's a risk for her to hang such orders, since that silly cook can sometimes come up with numerous excuses not to make an ordered dish or offer substitutes. But she must take the risk of being rejected nevertheless. If she doesn't, someone else will eventually hang orders on his wheel which he will respond to.

It behooves her to place her orders as attractively as possible. He has to feel somehow compelled to respond to her wish and her empowering strength and the smell of success in his nostrils. Orders placed in a nasty, bitchy manner are rarely filled with success, and such dishes are often quite bitter.

As for him, if he doesn't cook up something palatable and more in time for her, she'll just find another cook who will. It's a tough game, a dangerous game, and sometimes fires break out in the kitchen, cooks are replaced, waitresses quit or the diner just goes out of business. Yet it's all worth the risk, most especially when each one gets his/her act together. Then the result is *Babette's Feast.*

Better still, you guys, don't be a short order cook. Be a grande chef! If she orders a muffin, bake her a cake! Make it so rich and satisfying that she can't eat it all. Remember women are satiable, and with such a gambit you'll not only get a break from your labors but a juicy piece of the cake and then some, for yourself.

We reiterate that women are also producers and men, consumers. We are not talking about exclusivity here! As a matter of fact women can and do respond to other's women's calls.

Many women are heavily involved in production these days, and often wear two hats, as bread-winner and home-maker. They can do this, and they often do it very well. Yet most women in such situations are literally up to their necks in production (even more so than their male counterparts), which is not without its consequences and emotional bills to pay. There seem to be more and more studies and reports substantiating the negative effects and pressures of life-styles without appropriate consumption.

We're not just talking about a guy helping out in the kitchen, although such would not be remiss. Nor are we advocating a return to previous times, when anything other than home-maker, mother, or wife as a woman's role was frowned upon. We only point out that there really needs to be adequate consumption on the part of a woman to be fulfilled. If she's working too hard at production and if she and her man aren't true experts at this complex and dangerous man-woman game, things can and do turn sour in time. Fatigue and resentment become the rule, often leading to more serious complications.

If a woman in a relationship wants to be productive, it's also up to her man to assure and support that goal. Again there's nothing wrong with this as long as her great need to consume is satisfied.

Having said this, let's get back to the consumption phase of the cycle. He has responded to her call and produced what she has called for. It's now up to her to enjoy and consume the fruits of his labor. She has to overcome her intrinsic resistance to pleasure and any associated guilt, then sit back and enjoy her consumption. She will do this, assuming that he has produced *exactly* what she wanted. Any deviation or substitution, no matter how *small* in his view may subvert this pleasure producing sequence[6].

Let's clarify that statement some. In this context it is not always possible for the man to produce that diamond ring on demand, for example. Producing the ring is fine, if it's possible. Yet what we're essentially talking about is the importance of a man's genuine pursuit of his woman's goals and wishes. It's difficult sometimes to be sure, because of the strong fears he

[6]Remember the potential problems which may arise because of different languages, different thoughts, in this context.

may have regarding his production potential. It may feel as if she's asking for that glass of water in the desert! But delivering a want doesn't necessarily have a timetable. It shouldn't and mustn't! So a woman, if she's smart, may never find that ring or decide on a trip, i.e. reach the end of a quest. Yet the more a man can produce his woman's goals, the happier they both will be.

A fellow can make his gal feel like a queen by his merely wanting to give her what she wants. Let's say you're walking together down the street, see a special dress in the window of an exclusive shop, and you tell her how beautiful she'd look in it. If she responds with any interest, insist that she try it on. If the light is in her eyes and you reflect your love and approval of how she looks in it, then it matters very little if you can afford to buy the item or not.

Even if the money is there, priorities and/or values may dictate not spending it. If the money isn't there, the experience of your appreciating her attractiveness and your desire to please her (i.e. someday you hope to be able to buy her something so exquisite) will bring her such joy that that alone will deepen your bonds.

Her continued belief in your ability to produce whatever she truly wants is what enriches and empowers the relationship.

If she wants to travel to an exotic place, there are films, videos, books and travel agencies. Half the fun (and more) is in the dreaming. If she dreams of living in a fancy home or redecorating, visit those neighborhoods and talk about exactly how she'd like it all to be. It keeps the juices flowing.

There are all sorts of ways to experience life. You'll make her feel like a queen by just wanting what she wants. She'll return the favor by making you king. If a woman truly loves her man, she doesn't want to run him into the ground. She is well aware of his capacities which, remember, are often greater than he is willing to admit.

A woman is most attractive when she's consuming and having fun. A man really adores his partner when she consumes and truly enjoys what he has produced for her. It gives him great gratification to pleasure her so.

It is important for a woman who has had her fill (who has received what she has wanted from her man) to, so to speak, digest and assimilate what he has produced for her. She can't truly enjoy a sumptuous meal again if she's still full from the one before. Here digestion and gratification make room for more pleasure.

A woman's acknowledgement of her partner for his production makes him a winner. This is another important source of gratification for the man, and actually primes him for further production.

A woman who promptly gets what she wants from her man, will eventually slow down in her requests and be very careful and more accurate with them. There'll be less waste and confusion.

Even if she's a bit quiet and not calling, it behooves a man to leave the kitchen and take on a waiter's role, offering her a menu of delectables to choose from. Pamper her, offer her things, places, baubles, bangles and beads. Remember that within a healthy caring relationship a woman's happiness sets the level of the man's happiness. That's just the way it is.

A man can be quite productive. He can feed his appetites and enjoy his hobbies a lot; but if his woman is unhappy, all those things fail to truly satisfy him.

A woman's resistance to a given offer from a man may result from her fear of loss. She may also resist as a screening out process (to test a given man's true intention). Or, such a refusal may just be a reflexive initial response—just part of the game. A little persistence on the part of the man (assuming he's truly interested in her) is warranted in such circumstances—within limits, of course.

Of course either partner at any time may choose not to play when he or she perceives that this particular game has become unbearable for some reason. Just remember, however, that if you play by winning rules, by the principles we have been describing, not only will your game improve, but your joy in life will increase and the chances of either member quitting the game will significantly decrease, simply because everyone is just having too much fun, is feeling too gratified to even think of quitting.

Finally, it is important to note that the principles we have been discussing here to a significant degree also apply to children. The following experience will exemplify this concept.

Leo:

Recently while shopping in the super market I was quite taken with a mother treating her little son of about six in a most appropriate and enriching way. It was a small thing, and whether she was fully aware of it or not, she was treating him like the little man he was. She was giving him things to do, allowing him to produce for her, and acknowledging his accomplishments along the way. She gave him the job of picking items off the shelves and placing them in their shopping cart. The pleasure of his accomplishments was written all over his face and person. It was a joy to see people find so much fun in grocery shopping, not to mention the confidence this healthy dose of approval engendered in the child.

SEX, Food and Baubles

First, some important definitions:

SEX—in this chapter, refers not only to having sex or making love, but also to giving attention, affection, and to cuddling: in short, any act in which caring and loving both physical and verbal are applied.

Food—refers to the necessities of life, such as food, clothing, shelter, medical care, etcetera.

Baubles—refers to things and activities which we can (in reality) do without but so much enjoy: from ice cream and cake to fancy clothing, special meals and jewelry.

These are the major categories of interaction between men and women within personal relationships in the man-woman game. Remember we are talking about enrichment here and hopefully going from a good place to better and better. So, assuming that the absolute bare necessities of life are taken care of (few would be interested in sex if they were dying of thirst or hunger), these major categories are of descending importance in a relationship. That is, *SEX* (remember, this includes affection, attention, etcetera) is primary (category 1) with *Food* being secondary (2), and *Baubles*, tertiary (3). There is no contradiction here, since at this level in the Food category we are now talking about quantity and quality, not bare necessities.

A woman may have her mink and diamonds, but if she's not gratified sexually, if she's not getting the attention she so craves from her man, she won't be ultimately happy. Her bitterness may even spill over into many areas of her life and onto many people. This is the "bitchy" doctor's or executive's wife syndrome. She *has it all*: the big house, pool, country club; everything except enough prime time with her man. He's too busy giving her (and himself) those other things. On the contrary most women who enjoy a close, sensitive and torrid relationship with their men would be happy in a shack. They wouldn't consider trading their great relationship away for a mansion in the country.

Of course, there's nothing wrong with aspiring to have it all. Women, after all, do really want it all! As a matter of fact, categories two and three can be very important as enriching and endearing factors. We have more than implied their importance in our discussions earlier, whether we were talking about going places or buying things. When, in a relationship, category one is satisfied, two and three can be the icing on the cake: great sources of more pleasure, fun, and bonding.

It is at times when category one is unsatisfied or wanting that Food and Baubles may take on importance out of proportion to their intrinsic value. That is, they become key elements in one's happiness. That special vacation or piece of jewelry may become all-encompassing passions, even absolute demands in a relationship poor in good loving and affection. If she isn't getting it one way, she'll get it in another. Yet in truth this is a delusion. For the fulfillment of such passions is only temporarily and superficially gratifying. It can not really replace the gratification and happiness achieved in deeply loving relationships where great sexual pleasures are achieved, with a generous helping of mutual attentiveness and affection. A man, in fact, will actually get few points in substituting Food and Baubles for SEX.

At times, Food and Baubles may play a role in self-gratification. They can, to some extent, soothe and sustain us. How often, for example, have you consumed something sweet or bought something superfluous following a disappointment, or even at times when for whatever reason you just needed some stroking? But such acquisitions are but so much silver and bronze in our quest for the gold, and we would much rather receive such medals than purchase them for ourselves.

So much for Food and Baubles. Let's get into the most important category of SEX.

Leo:

Paula and I, as stated earlier, had a very active and satisfying sex life throughout our marriage, which has been totally monogamous. That doesn't mean that we've been oblivious to the rest of the world, that we're never turned on by others or haven't any fantasies that we enjoy. One needn't act on such impulses, and I can flirt with the best of them. Flirting can be a lot of fun, if one does so with well-adjusted fun-loving adults, who understand that such behavior needn't lead to anything else.

We've been married for 25 years, and have always been each other's best friend. However, as we learned to play the man-woman game better (to be more deliberate in ways which seemed to have come naturally in the past) so did our relationship become even closer and more loving, with less clutter and garbage. And as we practiced some simple (but not always easily applied) sexual techniques with increased and more accurate communication, Paula's orgasms have continually increased in intensity and duration. I always knew it was very important, but it still came as quite a revelation to me just how important good lovemaking and attention are. It became so good, exciting, and intense that Paula admitted she would really love doing it nearly all the time. Like that hungry kid in a candy shop, she had found such sweetness, she didn't want to let go easily.

She has told me and I've really come to believe (at

some level) that she wouldn't at all mind a drop in the quality in our life-style (some aspects of which she really enjoys—like good dinners out), if that would translate into having me around more. More time with her, my attention on her, more great sex is apparently more important to her! This was quite a revelation, especially since we are now at such a wonderful place in our relationship, both physically and emotionally.

At this point a lot of you guys may be feeling left out. O.K., I'll admit that to a large degree a lot of this stuff was strange to me too, and seemed quite one-sided. Sex for Paula and me used to be a few kisses, a little bit of fore-play, such as clitoral stimulation (I knew that was important) and finally intercourse—the objective, what it was all about. It was good for us both. I got mine when I came and hoped and assumed Paula had gotten hers. To be sure, she did enjoy it; but what she gets now (and me too) is a different reality—like coming from some bush league into the majors. I'm *not* exaggerating this turn of events!

Hollywood has perpetuated the awful myth that the heights of sexual pleasure are attainable by rushing to climax through intercourse. These ideas are so deeply ingrained in us it's hard to let them go. Don't believe them! Paula and I are now often amused when we see a movie these days where lovers trip over each other in the rush to remove their clothing and "get it on", have intercourse—quick, quick, we've got to climax—hurry up. O.K., I'm not saying it isn't fun at that level, but it's a drop in the bucket. Believe me, there's *so much* more to be had!

Some of the greatest experiences I have had were when I caused Paula to come really well! I felt incredibly powerful, confident and gratified following such earth-shaking episodes, a great place to be. Remember too, the "spill-over effect".

So let's look more deeply into what this is all about in practical terms.

For a woman to come well, to have intense and extended orgasms, the following things need to be in place:

1. The woman has to really want this experience; it has to be a major goal in her life. (We don't say this flippantly. There is very strong resistance to such pleasure not only up front, but also during love-making. This still occurs with me and Paula, and we'll touch on some techniques to overcome this later, when we talk about technique in general.)
2. The woman has to be in touch with her body, her sensuality and sexuality. She needs to learn what feels good to her. Sometimes this may happen by accident—just discovering something special during love-making. Yet a lot can be learned privately, through exercises geared to self-discovery: by touching, rubbing, and fondling herself both in the sexual and the sensual (skin) areas of her body.
3. A caring, loving partner, who has some basic knowledge in technique is required. All kinds of sparks can fly during mutual stimulation and intercourse, when these acts are performed with proper technique and care. However, the greatest intensity and pleasures are to be had when both partners' attention is on one body.
4. There needs to be active and accurate communication, both verbal and physical, during love-making. This is both more difficult and much easier than you think. Like riding a bike, it's very difficult at first, but once you get the hang of it, it comes naturally. Remember that in general we are all very touchy and vulnerable when it comes to our sexuality and abilities in this arena.

It can be difficult and potentially depressing, for the man, when a woman says, for example, "Honey that's a bit irritating, could you lighten up?" There is a danger of ego bruising here. Yet without such communication she'll just be turned off, and he'll never achieve his goals in relation to her. Or he'll think all is well, she won't be honest with him and he'll not know the truth. He may enjoy his climax but she'll be frustrated and resentful.

Paula and I still communicate openly and often when I'm "doing" her. I don't take it personally when she gives me an instruction, like "lighter", "slower", "left". This is so important because it gets me on the "right track".

Such communication during love-making needn't at all destroy the mood or pleasure. I'll admit, though, that it's very beneficial, stimulating and encouraging for the woman to acknowledge from time to time the pleasure she's receiving from her man during love-making. This positive feedback is good as a general rule because it keeps his attention and interest, and also makes him a winner.

At times, a woman may be enjoying her sensations and be so quietly focused on them, that her man might think he's just not getting it right, which can sure put a damper on things. By all means, enjoy and focus, but don't forget to acknowledge. A man should rarely, if ever, be in doubt about what's happening or his abilities to create physical pleasures for his woman. Such doubts are quite counter-productive and no fun at all.

A very effective ploy and sequence is to find him (her) right, then make a request and acknowledge his (her) compliance—for example:

Woman:

"Honey, that really feels good; could you do it slower? Ahhh, thank you, that's great!"

Finally, it also happens that a woman will want to do her man (bring him to climax through penile stimulation). All the things I've been discussing, such as proper communication and acknowledgement, also apply here.

Before Paula and I close out this chapter with some of our personal feelings and thoughts about this subject, let's discuss some important points about technique.

Certainly a woman's most intense orgasms are experienced through clitoral stimulation. This is achieved by using a well-lubricated finger. Ordinary Vaseline is ideal for this purpose, but other over-the-counter lubricants will also suffice. Remember it was mentioned that the greatest experiences occur when both partners have their attention on one body, i.e. the man does the woman or the woman does the man. Such an approach, of course, needn't be followed exclusively in love-making, but such experiences can be wondrous indeed. It's perhaps best to do what you feel like doing; a little experimentation and imagination are helpful. In general, these approaches are both applicable to men and women. Where there are differences they will be stated.

Let's go through the technique of doing a woman. First get into a comfortable position (usually lying side by side). Any position with which you're comfortable will do: both lying, the woman lying and the man sitting by her, etcetera, whatever feels right! Some teasing and non-genital stimulation (such as *lightly* stroking her thighs or nipples) is fun and slowly builds excitation and receptiveness[7].

[7]There are sensual and physiologic connections throughout our tactile senses, such that, proper, gentle stimulation (rubbing) of non-genital skin and mucous membrane zones, can evolve pleasurable sensations and heightened excitation in prime genital areas (clitoris, vagina, penis, testicles). Exercises and practice with experimentation, will develop such connections and enhance sensual pleasure as preludes to and during more direct sexual activities.

Adequate lubrication is important, as are well-trimmed nails. Approach the clitoris slowly and lightly, with gentle, slow strokes on it at first. Variations in strokes (up and down, side to side, circular etc.) and pressure may be employed.

In contrast, men usually prefer firmer pressure on the head (glans) and shaft of the penis while stroking it. A man will come to appreciate and enjoy a lighter, slower touch with more exposure to variations.

To some extent you then begin to play it by ear. Remember communication is the key: she needs to put her attention on the sensations welling up in her and to direct you in your manipulations. If she calls for a change, *don't* take it personally. *Do* comply. Also, it's up to her to let you know how good it feels from time to time. If you're paying attention, you will also sense and know what's working, by her physical responses. If it feels good to your fingers (a sense which develops faster than you think!) stay with it. If she's hardly moving, this usually means you've hit pay dirt, and she doesn't want to move you off the spot. There are "hot spots", "sweet spots" on the clitoris and in the vagina just awaiting discovery and stimulation. As one is well into this process, firmer pressures may be welcome. Variations in pressure and strokes are usually productive in increasing excitation.

It's time to talk about levels of excitation and the ultimate goal of intense and prolonged orgasm. This is achieved through "peaking". One peaks his or her partner by stopping the stroking movements and applying gentle but firm pressure on the clitoris or the glans. This is done for plus or minus 10 seconds, and at times when things are really getting exciting (i.e. orgasm is approaching, but not yet on the scene). By doing this (peaking) and then starting again with strokes, one is able to increase the level of sexual sensation and excitation to higher and more intense levels, many times.

At the time one's partner is finally taken over the top (brought to orgasm) through this peaking technique, it will be quite memorable indeed, and may be prolonged beyond what most consider normal limits. It is definitely possible to maintain an orgasmic state for quite a while, and even get to higher levels of orgasm during such states, through continued clitoral stimulation and peaking. During orgasm itself, a gentle and slow stroke is often very pleasant. Don't forget adequate lubrication! When removing one's hand for more lubrication, be sure to tell your partner what you are about to do. Surprise could interfere with the level of excitation if one is not forewarned.

One can also stimulate the clitoris and vagina simultaneously by using both hands, or a thumb and forefinger. All kinds of variations are possible. Just go with what feels good at the moment and enjoy it. The climax will happen, but before that there's an incredible journey to savor. Being too concerned with reaching orgasm misses much pleasure and many great experiences along the way. Incidentally, a great time to have intercourse is just after she has had a good orgasm. Both partners will really enjoy this since her vaginal walls are engorged (puffy, swelled) and well-lubricated. Mutual pleasurable sensations will abound.

When you decide to quit, it's important to bring her (him) down. That is, apply firm pressure to her perineum and clitoris with the palm of your hand or a towel (*do not rub*!)—just pressure. To bring him down, just holding his penis, especially the glans, firmly in your hand will do. Such pressure should be applied for plus or minus 30 seconds or as long as it takes, so that when the pressure is removed it feels o.k. to do so. Coming down has its own pleasures.

A few final points: We're all individuals, and it's really fun to discover and experiment with our sexuality, sensations and positions, finding just what and where it is that is most exciting for us. Anything mental, whether in the realm of sexual fantasy, expectation, or anticipation which would enhance the sexual experience, is really a fine maneuver to employ. Nothing is wrong with spontaneity, but some planning in this regard can only enhance your lovemaking.

Also remember resistance. Often a woman will resist going to higher plains of sexual excitation when she's getting done. If this is happening (if she's really in touch with herself, she'll know it and can communicate this) you can sometimes break through this resistance by distracting her through firmly stimulating the non-genital portions of her body as you maintain clitoral contact. For example, firmly stroking the palm of her hand or arm with your fingertips, or even the soles of her feet (no tickling please) might do it.

Lastly, a real orgasmic enhancer for both men and women is "pushing out". That is, as orgasm approaches and also during orgasm, instead of contracting or clamping down, push out, as if you're "going to the bathroom" (or delivering a baby). This act of pushing greatly enhances the pleasurable sensations of orgasm. It may be hard to do at first, because it seems so unnatural; we're used to tightening up, contracting and clamping down when we climax. Try, work on this and you'll be well rewarded.

Now it's time for Paula to talk about her experiences in this field, which will further elucidate the principles I've been talking about.

Paula:

Sexual experience for a woman, even with a partner she loves and is happy with, can range from a "turn off" experience to one of incredible ecstasy. Prior to taking the More University courses, my sex life with Leo was a satisfying and fulfilling one; but it didn't compare to much that I've experienced since. It's a totally different range of feeling, a new world! When I'm at a peak of sexual energy and sensation, what I experience doesn't remotely resemble anything I've experienced before! The degree of pleasure begs for a new word to describe it; and having experienced such heights, I naturally want more of it, especially since I understand that there are no limits to this ecstasy, but that it can continue to expand indefinitely. I, for one, intend to go on expanding it, hopefully until my last breath.

There are even other pay-offs. I had major PMS (pre-menstrual syndrome) problems. Increased pleasurable orgasmic experiences can mostly solve this problem. From the irritable mood swings to the intense menstrual cramping, heightened sexual response is a prescription which works. Others have had success with minimizing chronic headaches, backaches, arthritic pain, and other disorders, as well as with losing weight. The studies are still going on.

For my part, I'd like to be able to devote myself to studying my sexual responses full time. Since other activities intrude, I content myself with acknowledging my appetite, my true nature and acceding to it whenever possible and appropriate (in my mind). This includes several orgasms in a 24-hour period, when I'm in the height of my heat cycle, on a free weekend, or vacation schedule. At other times, I work in activities which help diffuse such sexual tensions such as aerobic exercise, lots of hugs from Leo and eating some rich chocolate. The affection/attention really works. It alleviates the ugly part of my unresolved sexual tension and brings me down enough to be able to enjoy the pleasure I can receive at a later point in time. Without such release mechanisms there's a real chance for an attack of irritability and bitchiness. These heat cycles are known to continue even after menstruation ceases.

If you men out there can stop whatever you're doing and put your full attention on your partner at such crucial moments, the rewards will be enormous. If you have a significant conflict, your undivided attention for a few moments will generally bring her down to a more rational level, where you can schedule an uninterrupted period of time to satisfy her need. For even if a woman thinks she needs many hours of your undivided attention to be satiated, it will usually take considerably less of your time than you (or she) might think. And if time isn't an issue, what would be bad about some days of fun with your lady love?

Experience has shown me that the most exquisite form of female orgasm is when both partners have their attention on the woman's body. The orgasm's center is the clitoris with possible expansion to a full body experience. However, there are times when I very much want intercourse, mutual stimulation or a whole menu of varied sexual treats only limited by our imagination. What's critical is both partners' (but particularly the man's) sensitivity to a particular appetite on the part of the woman. Remember, if there's something the woman wants in the sexual area you can bet it's a key to the *most fun the two of you can have at that moment.*

Sometimes I surprise myself by starting off thinking I want one thing, but it turns out to be something different that I want. By this time in our relationship, I can usually trust Leo's response to be right on target. I used to think that variety was the key, and if I'd just pull something different out of the hat, it would be the spice needed. Yet it works much better to relax and just respond to my sexual appetite. When you first begin giving her what she wants without regard to pay-backs, you might find that your lady will crave one focused "do" after another. This may feel to you like it's going to go on *ad infinitum.* Of course you're pleased to pleasure her so, but you're wondering about something different. Chances are she is wondering too and the next time you find your bodies pressed against one another, you may have an immediate, strong erection along with a desire to sweep her off her feet, onto the bed for intercourse without much, if any, foreplay.

If you do so, you'll probably find it to be one of your better experiences of love-making. Why? Because you were responding to her appetite—your production exactly fitted *her* desire (not the other way around).

A word of caution here: A man has the choice of responding or not responding to a woman's call, of responding or not responding to his erect penis. By the same token, no matter how much a woman may be "calling" biologically, if her mind and mouth say "no", it's her right not to respond. That right needs to be respected fully. This is not to be confused with fantasy "games" that a loving couple may choose to act out. Unwanted physical, sexual attention is felonious assault. And there are times when a woman merely tests her sexual power by turning men on without any need or desire to follow through! Of course this can be a bit of a tease, but it doesn't warrant assault. The human race wouldn't have lasted so long without such feminine power.

There are certain times of the month when a woman is more likely to be "in call" than others. One is approximately 3-4 days prior to ovulation and the other is just prior to, during and immediately after menstruation. These periods of heightened sexual excitement are recognized by their elevated levels. The ideal is to manage your sexual tension at that level where loving, cuddling and good sex can be enjoyed. If you do this, your relationship will be blissful and have the potential for heightened pleasure in love-making, because these are the times when you have the greatest opportunity for expansion of sensation and extension of orgasm itself. This is because of the heightened excitement you begin with. If you allow the sexual tension to accelerate (with improper attention to what's happening or gratification) the turn-on changes into irritability and depression. Thus, instead of the best love-making you've ever experienced, you'll encounter some of your best arguments.

Heat cycles occur even after the cessation of the menses. Proper acknowledgement of a woman's sexual needs is probably the best prescription to get her through the symptoms of the "change of life". If a woman is alone, without a partner, it behooves her to learn self-gratification (masturbation, etcetera) for a healthy physical and mental well-being. Additionally, while it may not be good for weight loss, the consumption of chocolate or other gooey, sweet or fried foods may alleviate some mental stress. The latter, when combined in moderation with exercise and self-gratification, can help to alleviate sexual tension without causing unwanted weight problems. An occasional Hershey bar will do.

What you men can do to improve the relationships you have with female co-workers and friends is to make genuine and simple acknowledgements of how pretty so-and-so looks or "what a lovely smile". In other words, you've got to give these women some attention that can't be misunderstood as a "come on" or as sexual harassment.

Women love to be appreciated as women as long as they don't feel threatened or feel as if they need to respond in either a positive or negative way. Acknowledgement of their work is well appreciated in the work place. For loving relationships, lots of warm affectionate hugs will get the sexually tense (in heat) woman from one love-making session to the next.

For more pleasure, it's critical that both partners find the woman's sensations right at any given moment. Her body has all its intended parts, and works perfectly; so if she's not experiencing orgasm, that isn't because anything is wrong with her. (The exception here is severe emotional problems, which are not within the scope of this book.)

Sensations vary to a large extent from woman to woman, as well as within the same woman at different points in her cycle, and even from moment to moment within a make-out period. Communication is the key. She has to be in touch with her own body enough to know what feels good, so that she can break it down clearly enough for her partner to understand. It will feel even better when she's passively accepting such physical stimulation (allowing it all to happen to her).

Masturbation for pleasurable effect, where orgasm is not the goal but rather the enjoyment of each stroke, will make a woman aware of what maneuver is ideal at a given moment. Pressure (light to heavy), the speed, the type of stroke (circular or long), finding special hot spots, are all wonderful variables to play with. Sometimes I'm excited enough to enjoy hard pressure fairly early on, but lots of times I want slow and feather light touches. Sometimes almost touching, then not touching, in a teasing way helps to titillate and get me more excited.

Men will get more out of a "hot spot" by teasing in this way—sometimes touching the spot, to reassure her that you know what she likes, then deliberately going around it some of the time. You'll feel her body reach out to your fingers for more. A word of caution: finger nails must be carefully trimmed and hands well cared for, because a small rough spot can quickly become abrasive.

I remember once when I was having trouble discovering which part of the stroke I liked best. I was lying there with Leo rubbing me, and I asked him to slow way, way down. It was a revelation to me that I could clearly notice the approach to a higher sensation, and I could identify it for us both with a "there, there" each time he approached it.

Often a millimeter, a tiny, tiny movement to the left or right, up or down, can make a *monumental* difference to a woman. It sure does to me! Also, the size of the movement matters. Sometimes I want Leo to stay on a very tiny spot with hardly any movement at all. Sometimes a long stroke hitting a couple of "hot spots" is preferred: including motion inside the introitus (entrance to the vagina) in combination with the clitoris.

Men tend to think harder and faster is the key, when actually slower and lighter *may* be more stimulating. This is true especially in the beginning, but sometimes later on, too. There are lots of different motions to try, but when you find something she likes, stay with it as long as it feels good to your fingers. If your attention is truly on her, you'll recognize those times when peaking is indicated and stop your motion for a moment. You may ask her if she'd like a specific change. For example, "Would you like it harder?" If she says "yes", gently comply. A little later you may want to ask again: "Would you like it harder?", and so on until you get a "no". The same holds for softer, longer, circles or anything else you can think of. Or you may just change your stroke, looking to her for her response. With experience you will find yourself responding to her body with fewer or even without verbal cues. Throughout, acknowledgement (thank you's) for his complying with your wishes are in order.

The clearer the communication, whether vocal or physical, the better the sensations she will experience. Be sure to use plenty of lubrication and always warn her if you're going to change, remove your hand, or need to adjust your position.

I've experienced a great range in desires for different approaches, in connection with my moods and/or at different stages of my monthly cycle. A long, long time ago, Leo might've rubbed on me some, not gotten what he thought was an adequate response, decided there was something wrong with me, and quit. A woman can change her mind about what she wants after just a few strokes. That's allowed! But what I'm describing is something different. I was enjoying what Leo was doing, but not to a degree that he could recognize. If I had acknowledged what was good about his approach, and perhaps added some suggestion of where to go from there, we would have progressed to "better" quickly. Even the acknowledgement alone perhaps would have motivated him to some further creative production.

At some times during the month, it takes more subtle exploration on Leo's part before I can *lock in* to what feels the best. Once I can, Leo has got me totally in his hands, and is able to pull the orgasm from me any number of ways. He gets to choose. By then, I'm in an orgasmic state, contractions come naturally without any attempt to force them or need for me to be in control. It's sweeter for me not to be. What happens next is up to Leo. That special place of surrender is truly delicious. Leo can then choose to bring me down (which is pleasurable if done slowly and carefully, in stages) or decide to let me stay there until I've acknowledged that I've had enough. There is also the possibility of going to still higher levels in this orgasmic state. I think of there being little doors up to higher and higher levels, with the sensations becoming more and more incredible (it can't feel this good!) and the opportunity for a longer and longer stay on each level. Breaks are fine; it doesn't take long to get right back in. Leo tells me we've had these experiences for well over an hour: a spiralling upward orgasmic state with increased sensations. I have no sense of time. At those moments, I just want to stay there forever, or at least until I've had enough.

Enough would be when the sensations begin to feel uncomfortable, when the clitoris has experienced all it can at that moment.

Instead of sexual arousal hitting its climactic end in a release of tension notable by its clamping down of pelvic contractions (the way it used to be for me), I now experience the doors opening to new levels where the body relaxes, reaches out (rather than clamps down) until it pulsates without any conscious control on my part. This sensation can go on for long periods of time with varying degrees of arousal. With the help of your skilled partner and good communication you can extend these intense pleasurable sensations from the genital area to other areas of the body, all the way to your toes. The experience is that of a rosebud opening to full flower with its innermost juices becoming one with the leaves, the stem and the air. For me, it has represented a true surrendering of myself to Leo, an offering of my essence. When this is combined with some other sexual act (such as intercourse) it has felt like a true merging of our beings.

Leo:

I too have had some special sensual experiences and revelations which I feel are important to share.

Paula has done me a few times. I've enjoyed those times of longer pleasurable periods leading to ejaculation, as well as more intense ejaculations when I'm finally brought over the top by her. Also, I've enjoyed being brought down after climax. It feels really good to have that gentle but firm pressure on my penis after such climaxes. In being done, I'm talking about Paula's and my attention on *me*, not mutual stimulation.

I lie there with Paula comfortably sitting beside me and stroking my lubricated penis up and down with one hand, while holding the base of the penile shaft with the other.

There are "hot spots" for a man too, on the penis and other genital areas. There's much pleasure in discovering these special spots. Trust and accurate communication, as usual, play important roles.

I haven't been done too often, and I have a lot further to explore in this area. This is just fine. Yet, it's important to discuss why my getting done has been infrequent to date.

Firstly, I get a lot of pleasure and gratification in other ways. I really enjoy climaxing through intercourse after having done Paula. That's lots of fun for both of us. I also enjoy coming via mutual stimulation.

Also, while I'm doing her, pressed up against her, I get excited as she goes to higher and higher planes of sexual excitation. Her quivering body stimulates me almost in the same way as her stroking and peaking me do, though at a lower level of intensity. It feels good and in this way, I also extend my pleasure and prime myself for better climaxes when I've finished doing her.

Of course, my excitation through stimulating Paula happens during mutual stimulation at still higher levels. We've been enjoying things this way so much that there's currently less interest in doing me more frequently.

There's another important point. Men, every bit as much as women and more, resist pleasure. That includes me. I find that I'm not at all comfortable giving Paula the responsibility and power to pleasure me. I'm just reluctant to lie there passively and let it happen to me. So the times that this has occurred have been, I believe, most often coupled with Paula's spill over. At these times she has had very definite intentions to do me and to pleasure me. Such forcefulness on her part has broken down my resistance and they've been very special times.

It should be clear from the discussions and personal experiences shared above, that women in our society are taught from early childhood to sit on their sexual appetites. It is a fable that men bring sex and women bring the romance into a relationship. It is a fairy tale, a cover story to obstruct a woman's true sexual identity. Women are highly sexual beings and men can be very romantic, given the opportunity to break out of their cultural molds. Such training and cultural paradigms develop into all sorts of inhibitions and resistances to sexual pleasure in maturity. If one can learn to break through these cultural handicaps with new attitudes and techniques, there is a wealth of pleasure to be enjoyed. There is nothing wrong with this goal! The capacity to feel pleasure is built into us; it is natural. Discontentment and irritability can only breed more of the same. The joys, happiness and satisfaction engendered by good sexual experiences can only spill over to others in positive, loving ways.

When a woman is ecstatic about her sexual experiences, her man is a big winner. He is truly triumphant!

THE ROAD TO FULFILLMENT

4

Reality resides in consciousness. What one's attention is on is what one gets.

L.G.

It should be obvious that we have been sowing seeds alongside the road to fulfillment throughout this book. Hopefully some of these seeds have by now already taken root, and have blossomed, despite their existence in potentially hostile environments.

Such blossoms act as beacons to guide and keep us on this cherished road. We've talked about, and you know, how easy it is to go astray. We truly need all the "light" we can muster.

There are of course other guideposts on this road, which help keep us from straying into the wilderness of loneliness and despair. It is to these other guideposts that we address the following chapter.

Levels of Gratification

This is where it all begins, with you. Our book is about relationships, the man-woman game, but loving someone else requires that you love yourself. You can't give others what you don't have. Self-approval is essential to one having pleasure. One has precious little joy to give others when one is not gratified, as the shelves of pleasure are quickly depleted when one's inventory is low to begin with.

We all attempt to expand our sphere of gratification to include others. That is, we attempt to gratify others beyond ourselves whether it be our significant other, family and friends or the world at large. Such movements beyond the self to ever expanding levels of gratification are most nourishing, fluid and successful when we have a healthy amount of self-esteem and surplus of gratification in place. To be sure, without surplus and even from a position of scarcity we can to some extent gratify others, but this is bound to bear diminishing returns and sometimes there are significant bills to pay.

For example: It's the weekend and—

Carol:
"Honey, would you mind going with me and helping me shop for some clothes? They're having a sale and I could really use your input."

Ted:
(After some resistance and discomfort) "O.K., let's do it, but that's it!" (What he's really thinking and feeling is—"Damn it, I work hard all week; here it is the weekend and I still can't relax. I'll do this, but I'll be darned if I'll do anything else!")

The job gets done, but he's not in a good mood and doesn't want to be "bothered" anymore. Such feelings exude from the pores, rub off, salty and stinging into any nicks or scratches in the delicate skin of a relationship. Ted is feeling put upon. Had he been in a good place to begin with, the chance to help Carol could have offered an opportunity for more wins for him, assuming Carol knew how to play the game.

Giving to or doing for others can be in itself very self-gratifying and fulfilling when there are no strings attached. This is the best way to give and usually comes from a feeling of surplus. The giver does so *for himself*. Acknowledgement for such acts is nice but not a prerequisite, nor does the lack of such acknowledgement diminish the gratification experienced.

The importance of caring for oneself first is far from a new concept. Most of us have heard or read about it at other times. It cannot be stressed too strongly as critical to one's happiness and success in the man-woman game. Bonding and fulfillment for a couple, assuming there is a *surplus* of gratification within the relationship, will be enhanced when such surplus spills over to others.

We will, in some ways, be addressing modes of behavior which may be helpful in developing that critical mass of surplus gratification as this chapter unfolds.

Responsibility and Intention

When I was a young man dodging the slings and arrows of life and battling its injustices, my father told me I could do and become whatever I wanted. Baloney! Certain things just weren't possible! I could never do this or that, I just didn't have the ability, or so and so wouldn't allow it, etcetera. No one was going to convince me that the perceived shortcomings which existed in my life were actually for me to alter. I would have gotten a better grade had that teacher not graded so harshly. I would have gotten that job had the interviewer not been prejudiced. How about this one: I wouldn't be feeling so cold if that darn wind wasn't blowing so hard! (Might I have dressed more warmly?)

We could all fill volumes with such lists of "assigned authors", people or things to whom or which we give the power, the authority to help us attain or thwart our goals.

Very few of us are willing to accept the responsibility for things that go "wrong" in our lives. It has been many years since my father's preaching. The truth is, he was basically correct. Many limitations are self-imposed. Now, I'll admit that not everyone could become chairman of the board, but many more could *if they really wanted to*!

Here's a key element—intention. True intention attains! We are very much responsible for who we are, what we are and what we're doing in life. There are always choices. "Bad" things may and do happen to us, but we have the power to control our response to such events.

If we relinquish the power over our own lives, the responsibility for where we are, we lose control and become victims. We allow life to victimize us. There are people who love to swap stories of their victimizations and feel sorry for themselves. This is fine, if this is where they want to be. But blaming others and circumstances for their problems just doesn't hack it. We ultimately do *what we want to do*. If we didn't want to, we wouldn't be where we find ourselves. Once in that spot, we can just go ahead and blame the world, the stars, or the gods for being there—right?

O.K. Be unhappy! But who's really putting you there?

We even have more influence over others than we realize. To get what you want from someone, simply make it very good for them to do what you want; or very bad, to stop them. The intensity for such action on your part need only be beyond your subject's resistance (no need to use a sledgehammer to drive a nail).

This may sound glib and exaggerated. Yet the bottom line is that if you step into that puddle, you have only yourself to blame for the discomfort of your wet feet. You could have avoided it, worn rubbers or, after the fact, put on a dry pair of socks. There is no need to walk around with wet feet. Granted there are difficult obstacles in life. Sometimes they are the spice of life; sometimes, quite painful. Yet we all have the power to rise above such "challenges" and take responsibility for our lives, move on, move up from there. I'm talking here about responsibility, not total control. If, in fact, we had total control over ourselves, our environment and others, life would be a bore! Things do happen!

So what can we do?

If you *really* don't like the role you're in, stop playing it. Like what you get or get what you like! Accept things, fix them, or lose. Sometimes we may just want to lose, but then we should acknowledge our responsibility for such and go on.

Do stop for a moment and think about your life and who *really* made the choices that put you where you are. Paula and I have discovered, quite to our surprise, how we were directly instrumental in the course that our lives have taken.

Think. Isn't it so, that many people from humble origins achieve much, and that the reverse is also true? Is it just luck or circumstance?

Acceptance of these principles of responsibility may be difficult at first. Yet once you do accept and embrace these ideas, you will be empowered to break through all sorts of self-imposed, stifling limitations. The experience is truly invigorating, a life-expanding breath of fresh air. This will enable you to attain many of your goals, if you truly intend to achieve them.

Leo:

I felt compelled to become a doctor. It was always assumed by my parents and myself that this would be my destiny. From earliest childhood onward I heard often of the glories of medicine.

However, despite the fact that I did well in college, admission to medical school evaded me, or so it felt back then.

So I spent one year doing post-graduate biology work. While there, I continued to apply to medical schools, not only in the United States, but also in Europe. Yet the sense of failure persisted as again I was not admitted to an American school, even though I was now excelling in graduate school.

However, I *was* accepted to a number of European medical schools, and ultimately decided to go to the University of Amsterdam, in Holland.

I felt terrified at the prospect of being far from home, alone, in a foreign land, where they spoke a foreign language. Furthermore, there was the daunting prospect of the enormous task that lay ahead: becoming a doctor.

Yet I felt compelled to go. This was expected of me, I thought, and I had no choice.

The first six months confirmed my fears. Lonely and depressed, I relished crossing each day off the calendar as though it would hasten the approach of summer.

Yet there was never any hesitancy about my resolve to accomplish what I had come there for. And gradually, over the months, I began to develop an increasing familiarity with and appreciation for my environment. I found life less painful. I made friends and became proficient in the language. Indeed, I came to love my adopted country.

Thus, by the end of my tenure, not only had I excelled in my studies and graduated as a doctor of medicine, but also I had undergone a major transformation. Looking back I realize how the experience changed me in ways both unforeseen and wondrous.

At the time I thought I was doing these things because it was expected by others. My mother always wanted me to become a doctor. This was obviously her call and my response. Yet, looking back I now realize I was also actually fulfilling my needs to achieve this goal well beyond her call.

Today I fully realize that what happened was my choice. I chose to go. I chose to stay, not to give up, even though I was miserable for so many months.

Ultimately what appeared at first to be obstacles had become challenges, which, when overcome empowered me and enriched my life.

Even more wondrous, unforeseen, and enriching was my encounter with Paula. There we were, two kids from New York, unknown to each other and pursuing separate dreams. Yet somehow miraculously our paths crossed, over three thousand miles away from home. Not long after, we were married. In Holland.

Communication

We have stressed the important role that proper communication plays in nurturing and sustaining interpersonal relationships, and how when communication is inadequate, problems arise.

We all know and accept this concept. However, isn't it curious that despite this knowledge, we often do not communicate clearly?

If we discount those problems previously discussed such as different languages, ordering short, and codes, we still have strong tendencies to talk past each other. It's almost as if our spoken words were like so many wild little birds, flying every which way, difficult to perceive much less catch. Yet catch them we must in order to properly communicate and constructively relate to one another.

How do we do this?

It simply boils down to responsibility, intention, and attention.

If someone wants to pass some particular information on to another person, it is that person's responsibility to insure that the point gets across. This is not a passive process. It takes being in the driver's seat.

Following the steps listed below in a communication cycle will usually assure success. That is, your information will be properly received and understood.

1) Put your attention on the person with whom you are about to communicate. You'll be surprised how much you can assess about another person (for example: their mood, receptivity) just by carefully observing them. Eye contact is a good idea, when it's not excessive (intense eye contact can make people feel nervous). An individual will feel this attention. In a sense it demonstrates an interest in them and will usually open the path to receptivity.

2) The delivery—Impart your message, clearly. Gesticulations, hand motions, etcetera, may enhance your message, but if excessive, they will draw the other person's attention away from your words. So, try not to be too dramatic. In fact, there are some critical elements of your delivery which will either enhance or detract from your goal of communication. At the beginning, a calm, confident, warm tone of voice will support the process; a shrill, angry, loud voice will negate it. Also, opening with derogatory statements or ploys will be self-defeating. By doing this, we find the other person to be wrong with our initial contact and will be well on our way to losing their attention at the start.

For example:

Someone has forgotten to do something for me. I decide to remind him, and open my communication cycle by telling him how irresponsible he often is. At this point most people would be either feeling disheartened, getting angry, or both. In any case they would not be too interested in what else I had to say, much less in doing something for me.

3) Make sure your message has been received and understood. Check for confirmation that what you wanted understood is in fact understood.

4) Close the cycle. You'd be surprised how often we

leave people in "mid-air" by not clearly letting them know that we have completed our communication with them. For example a simple "O.K. See you later," might do.

On the other side of this transaction, if an individual is interested and wants the information being imparted to him or her, it is also that person's responsibility to ensure that the message is received. Certainly, if the communicator and receiver are both on top of the communication process, 100% success is assured.

So, as a receiver, make sure that you've gotten the message. Ask to confirm your understanding of what was imparted to you.

Also in this process it behooves the receiver to put his attention on the communicator.

One word of caution, which we touched upon earlier. It is often counter-productive to assume that one already knows or should know something. When such common assumptions are incorrect (as they often are), the lack of communication insures failure of the process.

The responsibility to ensure success in this critical parameter of interpersonal relationships (communication) rests on the shoulders of all parties involved. We must communicate properly or suffer the consequences.

The steps in the communication cycle above may appear to be mechanical, cool and devoid of spontaneity. Not really! The goal, after all, is to pass information clearly. If this is done properly, with both persons putting their attention on each other, it will succeed and also enhance the relationship. Besides, most of us really enjoy someone else's attention on and interest in us, whether we admit it or not.

Training Cycles

Most of us like to have it our way and get what we want.

We've already mentioned certain maneuvers to effect particular responses, when they apply to other people's behavior in relation to us. If you remember, we suggest you make it very good for them to do something, or very unpleasant, to stop them. Certainly the latter ploy, although effective, is hardly a method to win friends or create endearing ties. In either case the intensity and heavy emotional toll exacted by the actions above are hardly the stuff of daily interpersonal commerce. That is to say, such intense interaction can be exhausting.

How can we, then, get what we want from others, without turning them off, and in a more emotionally cost-effective manner?

Most especially, how do we accomplish this in the delicate context of the man-woman game, an arena so rife with confusion and potential emotional tension?

There must be a less demanding, "simpler" way to influence others to our advantage. And there is: the training cycle.

This cycle, although universally applicable, is especially effective when a woman uses it with a man. It is more easily applicable to a man, simply because he wants so much to succeed (to be a winner). A man who is continually (or too often) not winning eventually will become disinterested in the source of his losses.

The training cycle consists of three phases in the following sequence:

1) Overt approval: Find the person you're dealing with right. Make him or her a winner up front. This not only gets that person's attention in a positive way, but makes him or her receptive to your wishes.

2) Present the problem to him (her): This is what you want, want solved, or want to have done. It should be something that he (she) is capable of solving, producing, or doing for you (don't ask for that glass of water in the desert).

3) Generously acknowledge the successful completion of the task you ordered. Give him (her) a win. This makes their success with you real and very much worth the effort. It makes him (her) a winner, just the kind of stuff men, in particular, really relish.

It all sounds pretty simple, cut and dry. It isn't! Some care must be exercised when using such a training cycle. No one wants to feel manipulated or used. It really may not take much to get into such negative feelings.

Men quickly become uncomfortable if too frequently complimented. Women have a greater capacity for this type of acknowledgement. Certainly, in general, we're not used to compliments. Receiving them up front may make us suspicious. Once this happens, the efficacy of the cycle is in jeopardy. In fact the whole thing may backfire!

For example:

I may tell a secretary how nice she looks. Even before I make a request, in her face I can read the response—"O.K. What's he want from me now? Why can't he just come out and ask for it? I hate it when he plays these games with me." What an overblown result to a simple situation.

How can we avoid such negative results? Sometimes we can't! Yet we can nearly eliminate them entirely. We can do this by dealing with the other person openly and with understanding. Then use the cycle carefully and genuinely, with truth and honesty. No need to tell someone they look pretty when their hair is in a mess. Credibility is an important adjunct for the successful use of the cycle. That other person has to believe in you.

You will increase credibility if your initial step of approval is more directly coupled with your request.

For example:

I may tell a secretary: "That letter you typed for me, the other day, was just perfect, a really neat job. Please, when you can, I'd appreciate your doing this one for me. Thanks."

When you begin to use this cycle deliberately in a relationship, it makes sense to start slowly and build from there. By that we mean, don't overuse it, and keep your requests small at first.

The following will exemplify the positive power of the training cycle, as well as the destructive effects of not employing the cycle with due care.

Leo:

It's a great cycle and it really works once you're on the right track. Yet Paula's use of it on me, just after completing the Basic Sensuality Course, threw us into the greatest crisis our marriage has had to endure!

The course had been like a lost weekend: two full, intense days stuffed with information and at times quite emotional. I felt drained, nervous, and exhilarated, all at the same time. Could I really accept all these ideas? Could I give up some ego in the service of our relationship? Would I really be able to satisfy Paula sexually?

My head was spinning.

Paula, needless to say, was "hot to trot"—ready to take off. Like most women, she wanted it all and now. Although her various inhibitory influences were still in place (ordering short, fear of rejection, etcetera) the course was enabling her to overcome them to some extent.

She rushed out to Fredrick's of Hollywood and bought a sexy nighttime outfit, to turn me on.

Then she began quite deliberately and unreservedly to use the training cycle on me.

I wasn't all that receptive and started to feel pressured, even used and manipulated. I became more and more upset with the way things were evolving.

Furthermore, I started not to believe the things she said to me. "She doesn't really mean those nice things she's saying," I thought, "She's just using them on me to get her way." Finally and most unsettling was the next "logical" step in this thinking: "How can I believe *anything* she says anymore? It's just her attempt to manipulate me!"

Our marriage had always rested firmly on a strong foundation of mutual honesty, trust and love. This foundation was being shaken to its core. Painful cracks were appearing as we spiralled more deeply into this crisis for a couple of days.

Like leaves in some dark whirlpool we were being pulled down. We sat for hours, together, staring at each other, at the walls, trying to pull ourselves up. We talked; we tried to make sense of what was happening, but there was nothing to grab onto that would stop our fall. It seemed quite impossible to stop it. Paula tried to reassure me, professing her love for me. To no avail. I just couldn't trust her anymore.

I fell into a heavy depression.

Paula was terrified and even suggested we go back to that point in our relationship where we had been before the weekend. Just forget that we ever took the course. But there was no going back. We either had to move on or break up!

We called friends for help, but no one seemed to have the solution to this painful and frightening nightmare.

Then, as if we had passed into the eye of the hurricane, in a flash it was all over.

I suddenly realized something very crucial! I realized that when Paula was using the training cycle on me, all she was trying to do was to tell me what she wanted! This was not manipulation. It was communication. That's all it was, although it was a somewhat contrived and structured form of communication.

When I realized this, I found myself perking up my ears and putting my attention on her whenever she found me right as a prelude to making a request. It served as a signal for me to take notice—an opportunity to do something for her and be a winner (her knight in shining armor). That old refrain "What a difference a day makes" was never more true.

These days, Paula's use of the training cycle works very well with me. I simply adore the way she plays with it, with me. She's so cute with this ploy. I know it's her way (and a very nice, effective way) to tell me what she wants.

This cycle, therefore, can be very effective in helping us communicate and experience more joy and pleasure with each other. It merely requires, as we said earlier, care and understanding.

You might also remember that we have already discussed its use in earlier sections of the book (see pages 82-83), although we didn't identify it as the "training cycle" per se.

This, then, becomes a very important principle and particular mode of communication. Use it by all means, carefully and lovingly on your road to fulfillment.

Overcoming Vulnerabilities

We are all vulnerable in our own highly personal ways to the people and events around us. The human spirit although capable of being indomitable, is also delicate, complex and fragile.

We are vulnerable because we develop disparaging opinions of ourselves. Such opinions evolve over the years, through our experiences and our personal interpretations of them.

Although other mechanisms may have played a role, a lot of these negative feelings occur as a result of our being trained with losses as we grew up. What we mean by this should become clear if you can recognize some of the following denigrating phrases:

"When are you going to learn to . . . "

"How many times have I told you . . ."

"You're just stupid."

"You'll never make the grade."

Sound familiar?

Many of us have particular vulnerabilities in common. Some of these are gender oriented and as such are of critical importance in the man-woman game.

For women, the most important area in which they are vulnerable concerns their attractiveness and desirability. In a similar way, men's doubt concerning their potential, their ability to produce, is common and ever-present.

Both men and women require continued reassurances from each other against such doubts.

Frequently however, men and women act in ways towards each other which propel such doubts from the realm of possibility into the world of reality. We discover, assume or think that the other person agrees with the doubts we harbor. This makes the doubts real.

There are many subtle mechanisms by which our doubts are substantiated.

For example, if a woman is craving some attention from her man (whatever the level), his lack of a positive response towards her will only deepen her doubt of being attractive. She will feel unattractive in reality and may even act in ways to support this negative feeling.

Likewise a woman's lack of support for her man merely agrees with his doubts concerning production potential. This will often result in his failing or just giving up.

Escaping from this trap of self-deprecation is no simple matter. It goes beyond the "I'll show you" response, since these doubts are deeply rooted.

It is important to be aware of these gender based, ever-present vulnerabilities. By being aware and also by being sensitive to our partners (responding appropriately to them) we may prevent the damage which would otherwise occur. Such an attitude is more than worth the effort and attention involved. The pay-offs are very significant.

We have made the point of how to respond to each other's vulnerabilities with love, attention and reassurances. Now, let's see how we might exercise some control over such self-deprecating tendencies from within ourselves.

Simply stated, we are *all* vulnerable in any area of our lives in which we find ourselves inadequate. Such feelings of deficiency may involve any area or field of endeavor in our lives. Some important examples which may also be influenced by gender are money (how much we have, our capacity to make it), appearance (do we accept and find ourselves attractive), sexual prowess, intelligence, and experience.

We are prone to interpret other people's reactions to us, whether verbal or physical, in terms of our sense of inadequacy. We are so assailable in this regard (finding ourselves wrong or wanting) that our own thoughts, without the aid of others, can trigger such failing responses or results. Negative thoughts, planted in mental pastures, enriched with self-deprecation, will surely blossom.

So, here we are, holding all sorts of feelings about ourselves. There is another angle, that being the extent to which we allow others (give them the authority) to influence our opinions of ourselves. We are prone to accept the opinion of those whom we respect, trust, or consider experts. If some "expert" told you that you looked awful and dressed like a slob, would you disagree and argue, shrug and go on your merry way, or just slink off to lick your wounds and figure out how to improve your image?

We often give much power to many "experts". The application of such power may play into and reinforce our feelings of inadequacy. Such experts may be "right" or "wrong". In either case they are only right to the extent we empower them to be.

It can be very difficult to get out of this trap we set for ourselves. These feelings are deeply rooted and our perception is such that they have often been *proven* correct. "You see, I knew he (she) wouldn't really care for me—how could he (she)?"

We may never completely rid ourselves of such negative self-images in every area of our lives. Yet, we can learn to significantly lessen the damage they cause.

It is important to recognize and acknowledge such feelings when they occur. Fighting them or denying them will not make them go away, and may in fact intensify them.

Acknowledgement, here, doesn't mean giving in to them in the sense of empowering their negative content. We're talking about simply recognizing your position, possibly even being amused at your human foibles, and quickly moving on from there. In this way, such negative thoughts may be handled quickly and efficiently. In so doing we will notice such feelings less often, particularly as we reinforce the positive in our lives.

If we truly believe that we are the best that we can be, at a given moment, we are then invulnerable! Rarely is such a goal—invulnerability—completely realized by any of us. Yet as we strive for and approach this goal, we will be less often and less deeply wounded by the "slings and arrows of outrageous fortune".

There is an underlying universality in human experience that transcends gender, race, and nationality. The more people admit who they really are, the more they realize they are alike, one to the other. Such empathy leads to a greater capacity to love oneself and each other.

We are all vulnerable under the sun!

Paula:

It's amazing! Here we are writing this book, living these principles. Leo and I. Yet I can still be frightened by the extent of my sexual appetite, awed by the amount of it, and fearful that I'm not attractive enough to Leo to get all that I want.

Feeling that I shouldn't want all that I do, I was irritable, finding myself wrong, feeling so vulnerable. Could it be that other things in my life were disturbing my equilibrium—my work, concerns about our children, parents?

"After all, we do make out a lot", said Leo, adding to my doubt. It doesn't take much for a woman to doubt her attractiveness, her most vulnerable zone.

I had to acknowledge it to myself before I could feel better. My appetite felt huge and insatiable, even though past experience had taught me otherwise.

My next step was to tell Leo clearly what I felt, so that there could be no misunderstanding. Our conversation took place over a quiet dinner out. I felt safe. I knew Leo would get the message. It was back to basics. It always goes back to basics.

That evening, after dinner, we had a super make-out session. What had been happening recently was that I had been experiencing a new and especially ecstatic "place" when Leo was doing me, and I got there every time. This was happening now, regardless of my level of turn on when he started. It seemed like that ought to have been enough. And it was! It was perfect! Yet I did mention to Leo that even though things were great, I suspected that I was ordering short from time to time.

Here I was, definitely in the "heat" portion of my cycle. Happening a lot these days! I felt irritable and jumpy about many areas in my life (even though Leo was giving me, on average, at least one orgasm a day). Sometimes we'd skip, but that was rare. That's why I mistook my irritability at first for other causes, sources other than sexual.

We woke up early the following morning on a delicious Sunday. It meant we could go back to sleep. I felt turned on and wanted to arouse Leo. He wasn't having any! But he reached for the Vaseline. (Oh, how I love the sound of the top popping off that jar!)

Leo brought me quickly into an orgasmic state, peaked me frequently, and he could have stopped at several times during that session. I would have been very happy. I thanked him several times along the way, acknowledging my fullness. But Leo continued for as long as there was feeling left. He continued well beyond what I *thought* I had wanted. When he finally stopped, he had me completely in his power. I would have done anything for him. He could have watched football all day! I felt so full and satisfied. All I wanted was to make him happy.

It spilled over into the rest of my life. My teaching, an upcoming musical performance, as well as other concerns, all seemed surmountable. I felt confident about facing whatever was to come my way and began to look forward once more to these other challenges.

Leo:

I had been feeling pretty good about myself, and here comes Paula telling me that she thinks she may have been ordering short sexually.

I bought this "criticism" of my production, feeling some pressure and mild inadequacy, but just for a moment. I quickly realized that even mentioning such a thing was really risky for her. She was wide open for rejection, especially since she was having such good times, so often. Still not often enough?

When someone has been starved all her life can she ever not feel hungry?

Yes, she can be satiated! We'd been there before.

I was determined not to be trapped by her ordering short. That morning, when I just kept going, kept on doing Paula, I don't know how long—certainly well over an hour, I felt very gratified. When it was over, she made it very clear that the day was all mine. Wow! Not bad!

Although I may have been a football nut years ago, I was not one now. I rarely watched much of it. But the play-offs were upon us and I was somewhat interested in seeing hefty parts of some of those games, assuming they were worth it (not blow-outs).

It was a pleasure knowing Paula wanted me to do that to my heart's content. She *really* wanted me to—for my pleasure. What a nice place to be.

I suddenly had a flash of insight. A woman can train her man with training cycles. Is a man giving a woman all and more than she orders a way of training her? An interesting thought. Something to ponder.

Yet whatever the mechanics, twists, turns and nuances, the result is what ultimately counts. Playing the game this way, embracing the woman's goals and needs, really works beautifully for all involved.

Going for the Good

All existence resides in consciousness.

Experience is what life is all about.

How and why do we react the way we do to our experiences?

We can't answer this specifically, as these answers lie in the particular experience of each person. Yet we can look at and understand some basic general mechanisms. When we respond to our environment, we usually do so in seconds or split seconds. Let's slow the action down, thus enabling us to see what really happens.

It all begins with *consciousness*. We are awake, aware, ready to respond to the world around us. Then something happens (an event, a *stimulus*) which causes us to have an *experience*. Nearly concurrent with the experience is our *judgment* of it (this is fun; this is awful; it's good; it's bad; etcetera). Our experience and our judgment of it create *feelings* in us to which we may or may not overtly *react*. Our reactions create consequences which may influence our future and leave residues (*memories*) which may also be influential.

This is quite a long story for just a second or two in time! It seems so automatic. Yet the fact is, there are various points in this sequence of events at which we have the choice to influence its outcome. There are a number of points, but at no moment is our power to influence greater than when we judge our experience. But let's stay in sequence.

As existence resides in consciousness, whatever we put our attention on is our reality. This is what we get. Or conversely, whatever we are unaware of, for all practical purposes doesn't exist for us.

At any moment we are bombarded by numerous stimuli from our environment. Our senses are poised and agile, responsive to sights, sounds, smells, tastes and pressures. Even our own thoughts can act as stimuli. Yet we are not sponges with unending capacities to absorb such stimuli. We automatically ignore many. Others, we choose to ignore, while selecting the ones on which to place our attention.

So, even at this stage we have a choice. Certainly if we put our attention on the "bad", there is little else. We are so often concerned with fixing things. Our attention is on what isn't right instead of what *is* right.

Remember, at any moment, what your attention is on is what you get, is what you have. We're not suggesting that you look at the world through rose-colored glasses or just stick your head in the ground. You needn't enjoy unpleasantness, but you needn't find such an experience "wrong", either. It's just part of life and mercifully so. If all were good, how boring it would be! There would be no choice, no chance, no point of reference or contrast. It would be all black or all white! Of course we are not omnipotent. Things we do not choose do happen. Sometimes they are quite painful and damaging.

Yet even in these circumstances we have the power to formulate and choose our responses to such events. Such water-shed events are a bit far afield from our current discussion however, which is concerned with the bulk of our lives, the day to day interplay of ourselves with others and the world around us. With daily events we do have choices, and most especially with the way we judge our experiences.

We judge our experiences in relation to our goals, prejudices, paradigms, self-image and memories.

The act of judgment strongly influences the way we feel about what has happened, which has an effect on our reaction and its consequences. It's like an action and reaction sequence. Yet we have numerous opportunities to direct the flow of our thoughts and emotional energy. We can build or destroy, nourish or deny. What one believes is his reality, is his life. For example, if you strongly believe that you're homely, even if others would disagree with you, you're ultimately left with your own image. Your opinion becomes your world and influences you accordingly. So what is the reality of it? Reality is like clay. It's always changing. We can mold it.

Even the world of science with all its "exactness" is like a bowl of jelly, shifting this way and that from the pressures of new discoveries.

Remember that the nature of whatever happens is determined by our judgment, our opinion of it. This is a state which is highly selective, fluid, and a result of who we are and what we're feeling at the time. The only absolute here is the great variability and potential for change. We can change our opinion! We might ask ourselves "can I win with what is? If not, can I change things?"

A key element in life is the ability to enjoy what one has. Good things tend to happen to happy people.

Another principle is to give what you want more of. For example, if you want more love, be more loving; give more love to others. How does it make you feel when someone is kind and giving to you? You're apt to want to give them something in return, even if it's unsolicited or not expected. The giver receives. It's easier said than done, but giving often gets us more, and in ways we don't always immediately see or fathom.

Functioning on the basis of one's prejudices creates distance, restricts potential experience and causes misperceptions. Finding someone wrong restricts your access to them and pushes them away from you. You can get out of such negative cycles with others by not losing sight of your goal of winning, and finding them right by accepting them for who they are. You may discover that they weren't quite as odd as you first thought. They might even turn out to be someone special, given half the chance.

The present is pure experience, what living, what

being alive is about. The past and the future, memories and dreams, are wonderful spices. Yet a spice cannot compete with or take the place of the main dish. Live your days. Putting most of your attention on the past or your dreams of the future will leave you very hungry and unsatisfied.

Finally, let us point out that boredom is essentially our refusal to put our attention on anything. Moving from a position of boredom, the easiest direction for most of us is toward discomfort. The situation often begins with self-irritation at being bored in the first place. Then it's downhill from there. Yet, boredom can be viewed as an opportunity, an open field. The key here is to get in touch with anything you can *approve* of.

Go for the good. You'll be surprised how often you'll get it!

Leo:

Picture this: Not too long ago, Paula and I had plans to meet friends for dinner at a restaurant. We've always had a mild compulsion about being punctual (less so these days), and are usually on time, if not early, to such things.

We arrived on time. Needless to say our friends weren't there. This was not good! There we were, anxious to get started, a bit hungry, fidgety and having to put everything on hold.

O.K., so we got seated and decided to get a head start on the menus and wine list. At the table we looked things over, including my watch as my sense of irritation slowly grew. Our friends were nearly a half-hour late by then and the evening we had happily anticipated was really beginning to sour. Why couldn't they come on time, or nearly so? We don't keep people waiting! They finally arrived shortly after that with a passing "so sorry".

We were happy to get started. Yet it took me about halfway through the meal to dissipate the undercurrent of annoyance within me. Not great fun!

That's not what really happened! That's what used to happen! This is what happened:

We still did arrive on time. Our friends weren't there, but knowing them we fully anticipated this.

We got seated. After taking time to relish the menu, we decided to share a delectable appetizer and some wine. We rarely indulged in this, but here was a perfect opportunity, not to mention a fun way to wait for our friends to arrive.

To heck with calories. We were going to enjoy ourselves.

What a head start. It turned into a time to leisurely unwind and to make contact with each other between delicious bites and sips. We set the stage beautifully for the rest of the meal and the evening, with loving glances through flickering candle light. We enjoyed it thoroughly.

Our friends arrived and we had a good meal in good company. No chips on any shoulder, no indigestion. A very fun evening,
and you know, it was all so easy.

SOME QUESTIONS AND ANSWERS

5

Q: *A woman asks—*

How do I keep my man happy and monogamous?

A: The best way to accomplish this is to successfully keep him in his role. That is, have him produce for you and acknowledge his accomplishments. This holds for whatever he's doing for you. Yet remember, nowhere is your fulfillment or his gratification greater than in his giving you pleasure sexually.

As a result, you will have surplus to give him which will be truly special for him. Such experiences will intensify your bonding.

Remember, your having fun, especially (although not exclusively) through what he does for you, makes you attractive.

Be as accurate as you can be with your requests, and don't forget to acknowledge his accomplishments.

Unless he's an incurable male chauvinist, he won't ever think "when do I get mine?".

Q: *A woman asks—*

What's so bad about my giving to my man? After all, I love him and when I cater to him, he treats me right. Isn't that what it's all about?

A: You're right! Your approach will work—but only superficially or for awhile, at best. It works to that extent because this is a time-honored and culturally acceptable approach. There are even those who would staunchly defend this stance as the natural and right way for men and women to relate to one another. We absolutely deny this!

Reinforcing the fleeting sense of happiness produced by this ploy is the fact that a woman will win some points (but never the game) from her man by treating him in this way. However, treating him like a "king" doesn't make him one. That feeling has to come from within himself; something that will never happen, if he's too busy consuming all the "goodies" that you lay out before him. This is in essence cheating him of his essential role and ultimate triumph.

Also, in such a way a woman is not ultimately fulfilling her true inner needs and desires. She is not playing her most gratifying role as major consumer in the relationship. This leads to huge gaps in the foundation of a relationship, which may eventually crumble at the slightest tremor, or rustle of another woman's skirt.

Indeed, the unearned power a man would have in such a liaison is potentially corrupting. Being waited on hand and foot by his woman has overtones of a of slave/master relationship. Such roles are demeaning. For the man, there is no true or positive triumph here. Just the potential for contempt. For the woman there is no true fulfillment, just more hunger.

Furthermore, if you look back to the question and the phrase "he treats me right"—it sounds like she's one step from abuse.

Follow-up Question:

Q: *Woman—*

I still don't completely understand this. If I cater to my man, won't he develop a surplus from which I will get what I want?

A: Yes, but surplus in this mode will be like so many scraps. It would be like feeding a starving person with a cracker. Getting what she wants in this way will never truly provide enough to fulfill a woman.

Although it may work for awhile, this is not a winning strategy in the man-woman game in the long term, nor is it nearly as gratifying for either party.

Let's get back to the major roles and dynamics of the man-woman game as we see them:

When a man gives a woman what she truly wants she is fulfilled. It really satisfies the "little girl" in her. In so doing, he is gratified and feels powerful. It's *his* accomplishment, *his* doing, by the sweat of *his* brow. The true sense of power and self-esteem achieved through meeting and overcoming a challenge cannot be acquired passively.

She is fulfilled and he is triumphant.

Remember too, that in time, she will have a surplus which he will cherish.

Q: Leo, you seem too good to be true! Are you ever limited in your response to Paula's requests?

A: Yes, if you're asking about always responding affirmatively, i.e. always trying to give Paula what she wants.

There are rare moments (a couple of times a year, at most) when the nature of Paula's requests of me are such, that my response is to flatly deny them.

These are usually rather touchy, sometimes angry moments, full of tension. They are often "knee-jerk" responses on my part, a fact which underlines their threatening nature for me.

Sometimes it's important to try to understand the underlying reasons for such negative responses to help resolve the ensuing discord they cause, sometimes not.

The point is that at those moments I can be as hardheaded as anyone.

What happens then?

Somehow we work them through. I'm sure the way that we do may vary. It may be a classic compromise, although I think this mechanism is rare for Paula and me, these days. Sometimes, Paula may feel so threatened by my blustering that she just seems to "bite the bullet". At other times, through our discussion of the problem, I "see the light" and change my position.

Whatever the mechanism is that we use to resolve such head-on confrontations, rarely, if ever, are there "bills to pay" or residual hostility. Our final adjustments seem to be quite sound and healthy.

Given the positive outcome from such confrontations, we may want to consider them another way. In terms of the man/woman concepts put forward in this book, it may have been that my intransigent positions were in fact actually reflecting Paula's desires, without her being fully aware of them at the time. Hence, whenever the dust has finally settled, there has been nothing to dig out of. It's truly been over. We have been aware of just such convoluted mechanisms and situations. At those times Paula contends that she realizes that I was just reflecting her to begin with!

Is Paula pressured into thinking this way because of my bullying and her emotional dependence on me? I don't really know for sure. We'll have her comment, momentarily. Yet I tend to believe that if such were often the case, as with any relationship where one partner's wishes were truly thwarted by the other, there would be large emotional bills to pay. And when there are too many of those piling up, bankruptcy in the relationship ensues.

I haven't received any of those big bills for quite awhile!

Paula:

Leo is right about two important points in his answer. The first is that there have been times that I have "buckled under" to his point of view. You may remember that even as late in our marriage as the crisis which followed our first Basic Sensuality Course, I (at least momentarily) was willing to go back to the way things were before the course. This type of response on my part no longer occurs. I've become much too confident an individual and much too convinced of the truth of the principles contained in this book. I *know* that when it comes to something I truly want, from the depths of my being, that Leo will produce it for me. He can't resist my call at that level, despite initial grumbling *because*: if its something crucial to me, I'll make that point clear to him, which is compelling enough for him to *want* to produce it for me.

The other point of reality in Leo's answer was that when these confrontations go away without any bills to pay it's because his stand, despite my protestations, actually reflected my wants. He in fact was simply doing his job by providing cover for my real wants, wants which for whatever reason, I couldn't face. It's Leo's ego surfacing when he talks about limits to his response. There are no limits. I have many goals that are involved with Leo's happiness and would never ask him to do something that would seriously thwart those goals. Nor would a situation arise in which I would want him to do something he would find morally or ethically unacceptable. It just couldn't happen in our particular relationship.

Q: *A woman asks—*

O.K. I ask him for what I want, but he doesn't give it to me! What do I do then?

A: Is he winning with you?

Check and see if you're asking him for things you *really* want. Remember, a man doesn't want to waste his production.

Do you acknowledge him appropriately and often enough?

To what extent is his particular fear of loss playing a role?

Your being behind him and encouraging him will empower him to get the job done. Remember, too, he may be a slow starter.

Also, it's your place to make your offers attractive enough for him to go for them.

If everything fails, he may be one of those hard-headed incurable male chauvinists. In such a case, it may be time for you to move on unless you're content with what you have.

Q: What's wrong with a 50-50 approach to doing things for each other? It's only fair—

A: Remember this is a union of aliens, not allies. Tit for tat works only superficially.

Keeping count is bound to result in problems in the accounting department and cause arguments. If you really want to play it this way, why not keep a timer in the bedroom? How romantic can you get? Gratification is its own reward. When a woman wins, her man wins. That's just the way it is! Stop counting!

Q: *A woman asks—*

I'm proud of my independence. To what extent will the application of these principles and my sexual awakening cause me to become dependent on a man for my fulfillment and pleasure?

A: *Paula—*

Remember that a man will support all of your most compelling goals if you make him a winner in the process. There will be ways for the man of your choice to support your independence and he will be gratified in doing so, when he sees that he's winning with you. Never forget to acknowledge him for his good deeds. It's not a question of losing your independence, but adding to your life.

Although much more pleasurable with a special partner, your sexual/sensual awakening can occur within yourself and with research partners along the way. Remember a woman first of all needs to be in touch with her own body. That means regularly performed sensual exercises of one type or another, which include masturbation for pleasurable effect (stopping just short of orgasm) and bringing oneself over the top. My current experiences with these exercises far outstrip many earlier sensations with a partner. So a lot can be accomplished in this regard all by yourself.

However, it'll always be better with a caring partner, assuming that clear communication is taking place.

Your work and all your relationships will benefit from an awareness and fulfillment of your sexual needs. Even if you aren't in a sexual relationship, you can greatly benefit from tending to those needs on your own.

Remember though, that surrendering sexually to a loving partner brings an ecstasy you can't experience elsewhere. If this compromises your freedom, that will only happen if you so desire.

Q: *A single woman asks—*

How do these principles apply to me, and how can I use them to help me find the man with whom I want to share my life?

A: The principles in this book apply to any transaction between a man and a woman whatever its nature, setting, or level of intimacy.

Men love to produce and are especially gratified when doing so for a woman who appreciates their production. This principle holds true on a first date as well as after 25 years of marriage.

What is irresistible to any man is a woman's compelling desire, if he senses he's going to win with her.

Enjoy the pursuit of your goals. Having fun is very attractive to everyone around you, including the guy you may have an interest in. Start him winning with you early by finding him right quickly ("I really enjoy talking with you; it's such fun!"). Whatever you do, honesty and sincerity are prerequisites. Put him in his role and allow him to produce for you. Enjoy your consumption and acknowledge him for the pleasure he produces for you. Do so honestly and caringly.

Gradually build on these successes. In time, if you so desire, he'll willingly become yours in body and spirit.

However, if you're continually coming up empty in the man department, start asking yourself what you really want. Although we all bring prejudices and other blocking agents into our relationships, an habitual failure to form a deep and lasting one with someone is a sign of a lack of true intention, or emotional problems which are beyond the scope of this book.

Beyond this, it *all* applies to you.

Q: *A woman states—*

A lot of these roles and dynamics sound so much like a 1950's approach to life—very anti-feminist and backward.

A: Remember that at the heart of these principles is the concept of a man embracing his woman's goals. Stop and think. If such truly happens, what more could a woman ask for at work or at play? You then, as a woman, determine what you want and what you get.

Is this not the goal of feminism?

We nevertheless are aware that the struggle for equality of the sexes is far from over. Many inequities still exist fostered by gender-based attitudes which persit in our society.

Although some basic concepts put forth in this book may initially appear to be anti-feminist, in fact, the opposite is true. These principles, when properly applied, are beyond feminism. They offer female fulfillment in interpersonal relationships well beyond making the grade in the corporate board room.

Within caring relationships these concepts afford a woman the opportunity to have it all.

Q: *A man might say—*

If I really follow the principles put forth in this book, I won't be a man anymore; I'll be a wimp.

A: Yes, you will be, to your macho friends. You will be running a menu by your women looking for that special something that will please them *just so*. You will place the goals of a special woman seemingly before your own. Yet, you'll know gratification like you've never experienced before. The certainty that you have the capability to totally fulfill a woman, if you choose to do so, gives you a power more far-reaching than any earlier conquests. When a woman senses your attention on her and your desire to please the little girl in her, you'll become irresistible. Then what stories you'll have to share. Your macho friends may want to know your newfound secrets of success.

We would cure many ills by
overcoming the epidemic of unhappiness
that plagues us.

L.G.

ABOUT THE AUTHORS

Leo and Paula Gorelkin's happy and monogamous marriage of 22 years was a testament to how well they had instinctually played the man-woman game.

Their exposure to the philosophies of More University in 1987 crystalized emotionally and physically their successful approach to life as individuals and as a couple in particular. Such realization led them on a path of ever greater fulfillment and enrichment neither would have thought possible.

The *Man-Woman Game* is a review of these principles of life and interpersonal relationships expanded upon and interwoven with stories of their own development and personal experience—a journey of incredible enlightenment and joy.

Leo Gorelkin, M. D. is a pathologist who works for a federal agency in Atlanta, GA. Paula Gorelkin is artistic director and pianist for a chamber music ensemble based in Atlanta. She also teaches piano privately. They are the parents of two grown children.

Together, Leo and Paula work as Enrichment Counselors to individuals and groups enlarging upon the information contained in this book. For further information concerning individual counseling or group seminars the authors can be reached by writing:

MWG
c/o Principio Press
P.O. Box 95-764
Atlanta, GA 30347

In addition, the More University staff offer workshops and give courses on this material in various cities across the country such as New York, Oakland, and Atlanta (to cite a few) at various times during the year. If you're interested in these, we would do our best to see to it that you received a current schedule.

ORDER FORM

Please send ______ copy(ies) of *The Man-Woman Game* to:

Name (please print) ____________________________

Address ____________________________________

City ________________ State ________ Zip ________

	QUANTITY	COST
Books @ $8.95 × number orders		
Shipping-Book rate $1.75 per book		
Air mail $3.00 per book		
Add 5% sales tax ($0.45) to Georgia addresses		
TOTAL		

Send check or money order made out to Principio Press to:

Principio Press
P.O. Box 95-764
Atlanta, Georgia 30347

Please allow four weeks for book-rate deliery.

Prices and availability subject to change without notice.

"... intriguing and provocative ... proposes a twist on the battle of the sexes that provides a win-win strategy for the world's oldest game."

Carrell Dammann, PhD.
Psychologist and Family Therapist

Leo Gorelkin, M.D. and Paula Gorelki

If you want to win any game, you need to know the rules. The man-woman game is the most complex, exciting, dangerous and potentially fulfilling game anyone can play. Discover the REAL rules of this game and its most successful winning strategies.

This book has it all — the ultimate guide to emotional and sexual fulfillment for the 90's and beyond.

— Goes behind the scenes by explaining how and why men and women unknowingly sabotage and damage their relationships
— Explains how to avoid such common pitfalls and empower lasting relationships of deepening commitment and joy
— Answers *numerous critical* questions such as:
How do I keep my mate happy and monogamous?
How can I get greater sexual pleasure without guilt and with my mate winning in t
How can I attract … to share my life?

Don't waste another … AN-WOMAN GAM
playing by rules and strategies that don't work.

READ THIS BOOK!

COVER DESIGN BY LEO GORELKIN, M.D.